Praise for *The Tapping Toolbox*

"*The Tapping Toolbox* is perfect for anyone who wants to get started using energy psychology approaches in their practice. Dr. Fred Gallo has created a deeply practical hands-on guide to using the tools of energy psychology for the main problems faced by clinicians and clients. My first introduction to energy psychology was from Dr. Gallo over 26 years ago. It ended up changing the course of my career. This book may just do the same for you."

—**Robert Schwarz, PsyD, DCEP,** author of
Tools for Transforming Trauma and executive director
of the Association for Comprehensive Energy Psychology

"Although tapping is covered in many books on the market today, *The Tapping Toolbox* uniquely advances this amazing technique. In this latest offering from Dr. Fred Gallo—the pioneer who published the first books on tapping and coined the term *Energy Psychology*®—you will discover a variety of ways to overcome issues from anxiety to depression to trauma and even chronic pain. While some books present only one way to address each problem, *The Tapping Toolbox* offers a high degree of flexibility by covering several tapping protocols, integrated with other powerful tools, to ensure that you get the results you desire. Enjoy and profit from the journey."

—**Tony Robbins**, #1 best-selling author of
Life Force and father of life coaching

"A quarter century after having coined the term *Energy Psychology*®, and after intense work with thousands of clients and students, Fred Gallo has distilled the basic principles of the approach into this clear and succinct, yet highly informed and sophisticated, toolbox."

—**David Feinstein, PhD,** co-author of
The Promise of Energy Psychology

"Fred Gallo's *Tapping Toolbox* is a concise, accessible guidebook for the mind-body interventions known as tapping, or *Energy Psychology*®, which can alleviate suffering from depression, anxiety, trauma, and more. Dr. Gallo's extensive clinical experience shapes his clear instruction on how to use these seemingly simple, yet profound, techniques. His case examples highlight the best of what energy psychology can offer: rapid, safe, effective positive changes. Find solutions to vexing emotional, mental, and physical problems through the state-of-the-art approach of tapping."

—**Lori Chortkoff Hops, PhD, DCEP,** president of the
Association for Comprehensive Energy Psychology

"With his *Tapping Toolbox*, Fred Gallo has created a precious first-aid kit. It's a textbook for therapists and a self-help book for all. I am full of admiration after 50 years of experience with therapy! This book is so much fun to read, very interesting, and an invitation to start working with these wonderful techniques. If you haven't already begun, start tapping yourself to health right away!"

—**Brigitte Michaelis, Dr. med. vet.,** Heilpraktikerin (health practitioner),
systemic therapy and kinesiology

the
tapping
toolbox

Simple Mind–Body Techniques
to Relieve Stress, Anxiety, Depression,
Trauma, Pain, and More

Fred P. Gallo, PhD

Published by
PESI Publishing, Inc.
3839 White Ave
Eau Claire, WI 54703

Cover: Amy Rubenzer
Editing: Jenessa Jackson, PhD
Layout: Amy Rubenzer & Gretchen Panzer

ISBN: 9781683734970 (print)
ISBN: 9781683734987 (ePUB)
ISBN: 9781683734994 (ePDF)

PESI Publishing
pesipublishing.com

Dedication

For Mary Louise Peluso Gallo (1915–1959) and Fred Patsy Gallo (1921–1983)

Other Books by Fred Gallo

Energy Diagnostic and Treatment Methods

Energy Psychology

Energy Psychology (2nd edition)

Energy Psychology in Psychotherapy (edited volume)

Energy Tapping (Fred Gallo & Harry Vincenzi)

Energy Tapping (2nd edition; Fred Gallo & Harry Vincenzi)

Energy Tapping for Trauma

The Neurophysics of Human Behavior (Mark Furman & Fred Gallo)

About the Author

 **Fred P. Gallo, PhD, DCEP,** is the author and co-author of several groundbreaking books, including *Energy Psychology*, *Energy Diagnostic and Treatment Methods*, and *Energy Tapping for Trauma*. He was the first psychologist to write a professional book on energy psychology, for which he coined the term. Since its inception, he has been a member of and on the Advisory Board of the Association for Comprehensive Energy Psychology (ACEP). He was also the association's president (2015–2016). Additionally, he is a member of the American Psychological Association and fellow of the Pennsylvania Psychological Association.

He has maintained a group clinical practice since 1977 and is also a professional speaker, having designed and presented programs to universities, educational conferences, and professional associations and organizations throughout the world. He developed a certification program in Advanced Energy Psychology (AEP) and has trained several thousand professionals in his methods. For more information on his work, visit www.energypsych.com.

Contents

Acknowledgments

This book echoes many aspects of my work over the past 50+ years. I would like to acknowledge and express my deepest gratitude to the people who have touched me deeply along the way and helped to transform my understanding of what makes us tick and how we may heal.

First of all, I want to thank Roger J. Callahan for introducing me to the unique understanding of how psychological problems develop energetically and how they can be transformed efficiently—or as he often said, "with great dispatch"—by tapping. His contributions will go down as Nobel Prize worthy. He brought amazing efficiency to therapy and self-help, as well as the willingness and courage to put his reputation on the line and to withstand massive criticism.

I am also grateful to John Diamond, George Goodhart, John Thie, Carl Rogers, Milton Erickson, Richard Bandler, John Grinder, Sydney Banks, George Pransky, Stephen Porges, and many others for their emphasis on relationship and mind-body solutions to physical and psychological problems.

Thanks to my clients and patients, who have teamed up with me in therapy, and to the professionals I have trained throughout the United States and many parts of the world. It is through practice and training others that I have been able to advance my own understanding and skills in the service of others. And thanks to those who have responded to this call and have conducted research, training, therapy, and coaching to help others.

Thank you also to Mr. DiMaggio, who helped me to develop confidence in myself and my ability to learn.

I also want to thank Kate Sample and the wonderful professionals at PESI for contacting me to write this book, and especially Jenessa Jackson and Gretchen Panzer for their remarkable editing and suggestions that helped me to make it even more understandable than I could have ever done on my own.

And most importantly, I want to express my love and appreciation to Carolyn for her love and patience as I took time away from our lives to do this work.

Preface

In 1992, I read an article in *The National Psychologist* that described a technique claiming to quickly treat addiction. The author, a psychologist, wrote that addictive cravings are basically anxiety and that his technique treated the underlying cause of the anxiety and craving, which he proposed was related to a bodily energy system. He claimed that this was the fundamental cause of addiction—more basic than cognition, behavior, chemistry, and brain structures. While much of this made sense to me in view of my clinical experience with addictive disorders, especially the relationship between cravings and anxiety, I found the treatment that he offered to be quite bizarre, to say the least! He would guide clients through a technique that involved tapping with their fingers under an eye and on their side below an armpit. After reading the article, I tapped at those locations myself to make sure I had it right. I then placed the article among a pile of papers on a shelf in my office and dismissed the technique as ludicrous.

I wondered how someone could come up with such a crazy theory and technique. I had read that this psychologist was an elderly man who lived in the desert in California and that he had specialized in treating phobias. I imagined that he had become extremely distressed about not being able to help people with standard psychological methods and, in his desperation, imagined that tapping was the solution to addiction and many other problems. I also pictured that he had long, unkempt hair and a beard, wore disheveled attire, and lived in a dilapidated hovel in the desert. I shook my head in disbelief, laughed at my musings, and went about business as usual.

Many weeks later, I had a session with a patient who had a substance use disorder. She abused pain pills, but she didn't have a pain problem. While we were discussing what triggered her desire to use, she began to experience a strong craving for her pills. In those days, we might say that she was *geeking*. I asked her to rate her craving on a 0–10 scale, and she gave it a 15. That certainly seemed to be accurate, judging by her appearance at the time. She evidenced slight tremors, significant changes in her breathing, and facial coloration.

I attempted to assist her by taking her through rational emotive imagery (REI), a technique developed by Maxie Maultsby that involves altering your internal talk and imagery to reduce emotional reactions. This settled her craving down to 4; however, moments later, when I asked her to think about taking her pills again, her craving shot back up. I had her do this several times, and each time the craving lowered to 4, then came right back up to 15.

I then remembered the preposterous tapping article. I explained to my patient that this might seem weird, but I wanted her to think about the craving while she tapped under her eyes, followed by tapping under one of her arms. I had her do this several times, going back and forth between those locations. Again, she reported that the craving went down to 4. However, this time a rather strange thing happened. *Baffling* might be a more accurate descriptor. When I asked her to bring back the strong craving that she'd felt before, she was unable to do so, even when she thought about her triggers and described the sensations of taking the pills. Her rating remained at a 4! Needless to say, both she and I were surprised and curious.

From a more or less scientific point of view, I had to admit that I did not really know what had happened. Was it the tapping itself that produced the result? Was it the fact that the tapping was preceded by REI? Was the patient so distracted by the tapping that even when she tried to recall the feelings, she would again return to the tapping in her mind? That is, did we produce some sort of ongoing distraction that REI could not achieve? Was this a placebo effect that could have been produced regardless of where she tapped while thinking about the pills? While my mind was filled with all sorts of questions about what actually happened, I realized that I needed to learn more. What would it take to assist my patient in totally alleviating the craving? After all, she was still experiencing craving at level 4, so some craving remained. I felt that I needed to investigate this procedure in more detail.

After scouring through the papers in my office, I eventually found the tapping article I had previously dismissed, and I decided to get in touch with the author, Roger J. Callahan. It turned out that he lived in Indian Wells, California—and not in a shack, but in a lovely home with his wife, Joanne. And, by the way, he was not disheveled and sported a well-kept beard.

I came to learn that Callahan had extensive materials available, including books, self-published papers and manuals, and audio and video tapes. I purchased many of them and began to absorb all of the information I could get my hands on concerning his approach. One of the things that caught my attention was the fact that Callahan considered much of his work to be proprietary and trade secrets. He had developed a diagnostic system that made it possible to determine specifically where the patient needed to tap in order to resolve not only addictive urges, but a wide range of problems, including posttraumatic stress disorder (PTSD), anxiety, phobias, panic attacks, depression, pain, and even substance sensitivities and allergic reactions.

However, the price to learn his diagnostic system was rather steep relative to most other training programs that I had participated in. Unwilling to part with so much money, I initially set out on a course of attempting to reinvent the wheel and possibly develop my own tapping diagnostic system. Although I succeeded in this task to a considerable degree, I later decided to attend training in the Callahan Techniques™, realizing that attaining knowledge that would allow me to help people was more important to me than money. Given all that I have learned and developed since that time, I am grateful for our friendship and the opportunity to study so closely with Callahan.

After publishing several articles on the tapping method, in 1998, I published the first professional book on the benefits of tapping for treating psychological problems: *Energy Psychology: Explorations at the Interface of Energy, Cognition, Behavior, and Health*. Quite a mouthful, eh? Since that time, I have published numerous works on tapping and energy psychology (EP) and have traveled the world teaching the many benefits of this technique. This current book expands the method, both for professionals and for individuals seeking a self-help guide. My goal is to teach you how to use tapping (and its variants) for yourself and for your clients (if you are a therapist or coach).

When reading through this book, I recommend that you suspend judgment and allow the evidence of your senses to be your guide, with some research thrown in for good measure. It is always possible to filter out what's different from what we already think we know. The trick is to set aside certain assumptions that get in the way of absorbing something new and to instead expand your understanding. And please don't just read this book and then put it away on your bookshelf or electronic reader and forget about it. Instead, apply the concepts and techniques covered, as I believe you will find this to be as rewarding as I have. With that said, I trust and intend that you will enjoy and profit from your journey. And enjoy your freedom as you tap along.

Warmest regards,
Fred P. Gallo

Knowing Where to Tap

We cannot solve our problems with the same thinking we used to create them.
—Albert Einstein

A factory's boiler was on the blink, and many experts had tried in vain to repair it. Then the manager learned about a technician known far and wide for his remarkable skills in repairing boilers, so he called on him as their final hope before having to get a new boiler.

The manager was taken aback on the day that the technician arrived, since the man wore a dress shirt, dress pants, and a tie—not the typical garb one would expect of someone about to do dirty boiler work. The technician also only carried a tiny toolbox, which couldn't have weighed more than two or three pounds. *Surely, he did not bring enough and big enough tools with him!* thought the manager.

Nevertheless, the manager greeted the technician and led him to the location of the monstrous boiler. The technician casually surveyed the boiler, looked at the various pipes and gauges, listened to the odd sounds coming from the boiler, and even placed his hands at various locations on the machine. After this, he set his toolbox on a nearby table, opened it, and removed a tape measure and pencil.

At this point, he did some measuring and made three distinct marks with his pencil at specific places on the boiler. He then removed a small ball-peen hammer from his toolbox and proceeded to tap on the boiler at the precise spots he had marked. Within a few moments, the boiler sounded better and began working perfectly! This amazed and bewildered the manager. *Must be a fluke*, he surmised.

The technician waited around for several minutes and then announced that the boiler should be okay from now on. He told the manager to contact him if the problem returned, but he thought that would be very unlikely. The manager scratched his head as the technician left the factory.

A month later, the manager received a bill from the technician for $2,000. This was very upsetting, since the technician was only at the factory for about 30 minutes and only tapped on the boiler with a tiny hammer. So the manager hastily wrote a note to the technician, requesting an itemized statement and expressing displeasure for being charged so dearly for, as he said, "simply tapping on the boiler with a hammer!"

Two weeks later, the manager received a note from the technician, indicating that he absolutely agreed that it would be unconscionable for him to charge so dearly for "simply tapping on the boiler with a hammer." As requested, the technician also enclosed an itemized statement as follows:

Tapping boiler with hammer	$10.00
Knowing where to tap	$1,990.00
TOTAL	$2,000.00

The Case of Mary

The following is a true story. Mary had a lifelong fear of water (aquaphobia). Although her hygiene was very good, she was unable to take a bath, shower, or swim, and even thinking of water caused her tremendous fear and tormenting body sensations. She also had frequent nightmares of being swallowed up by water. Mary's children used to beg her to take them to the ocean, but she couldn't do it due to her paralyzing fear. She breathed a sigh of relief when the movie *Jaws* came out, since her children quit hounding her about the ocean.

In hope of getting relief from her debilitating phobia, Mary sought the help of Roger J. Callahan (hereafter often referred to as Roger). For 18 months, Roger treated her with every therapeutic technique he had in his toolbox: client-centered therapy, hypnosis, rational emotive behavioral therapy, exposure and systematic desensitization, and even placebo techniques. All of these approaches failed. Eighteen months with every trick in the book—and nothing!

Well, Roger had been studying a chiropractic holistic approach called applied kinesiology and thought he might give it a try with Mary. This approach involves the use of muscle testing, bodily reflexes, and acupuncture meridians to examine and treat various health conditions. Acupuncture meridians are pathways of energy—assumed to be electromagnetic and subtle energies—that flow throughout the body. There are 12 basic meridians and 8 other pathways called vessels, as well as at least 365 acupoints. In evaluating Mary, Roger determined that only her stomach meridian was involved in her water phobia—and only a single point on the stomach meridian at that! Further details on this are covered later, but for now it's enough to know that the stomach meridian begins on the bony orbits under the eyes and follows a pathway down the body to the second toe of each foot.

After getting Mary's permission, he repeatedly tapped lightly with his fingers on the stomach acupoints under her eyes while he asked her to think about water. Can you just see it? Roger seated across from Mary, tapping with his fingers under her eyes, while she intentionally thought about water. Not what you would expect of a psychologist helping someone get over a phobia! But within a minute or so, Mary exclaimed, "Dr. Callahan, problem's gone!"

Shocked, he asked, "Mary, what do you mean, the problem is gone?"

"I don't get that sick feeling in my stomach when I think about water!"

Roger decided to test the results by asking Mary to go outside to the swimming pool, since he was treating her in his home office at the time. Here is how he reported the event:

> I fully expected her to resist as usual, but to my surprise, I had to hurry to keep up with her on the way to the pool. For the first time, she looked at the water, put her head near it, and splashed water in her face from the shallow end. I watched in amazement as she joyfully shouted, "It's gone, it's gone!"
>
> Mary's next move frightened me. She suddenly ran toward the deep end of the pool, and this sudden total absence of fear around the pool was so unusual for her that I shouted, "Mary, be careful!" I was afraid that she might jump in the pool and drown. She laughed when she saw my alarm and reassured me, "Don't worry, Doctor Callahan, I know I can't swim."

[Fourteen] years' experience with the treatment has since taught me that the treatment does not cause sudden stupidity. Respect for reality, I have learned, is not diminished by successful treatment. (Callahan, 1990, pp. 10–11)

That event was over 40 years ago, and Mary's previous lifelong debilitating fear of water never resurfaced.

What Is Tapping?

Tapping (also called energy tapping or meridian tapping, among other names) is a technique nested within the field of energy psychology (EP) that involves tapping with your fingers at specific acupoints on your body—such as under the eyes or on the arms, fingers, and collarbones—to relieve and even eliminate emotional distress associated with various psychological, behavioral, interpersonal, and physical problems. Tapping is used to rapidly treat phobias, posttraumatic stress disorder (PTSD), anxiety, panic, depression, chronic pain, peak performance blocks, and much more. You name it! Although that's a pretty bold claim, there is considerable research support for this wonderful approach, as well as my own and my colleagues' personal experience.

There are a wide range of elements involved in tapping, and this book covers the details of this powerfully effective approach. Here's an overview:

- **Chapter 1** discusses my personal history and professional work before and after discovering tapping. It highlights the discoveries of Roger J. Callahan and several others, as well as my own contributions to this field.

- **Chapter 2** focuses on the assumptions of this work and the importance of the relationship between the therapist and client, the client's objectives and goals, and informed consent. It also discusses the six phases of the therapeutic processes using the RILITA model.

- **Chapter 3** provides some details on the body's energy system, acupuncture, applied kinesiology, and treatment elements of attunement, measurement, muscle testing, psychological reversal, tapping points, supplementary treatments, words to tap by, challenging results, outcome projection, and debriefing.

- **Chapter 4** summarizes basic tapping protocols with an illustrative transcript detailing the treatment steps. It also discusses in vivo tapping as a way to bring this technique into everyday life situations. This is accomplished with the assistance of the therapist and by training the client in self-help tapping.

- **Chapter 5** explains how to overcome other blocks to treatment effectiveness, including building rapport, listening, persistence, flexibility, continuous tapping, and layering. This section also covers a variety of other treatment methods that have proven effective, especially for those who would rather not tap for various reasons.

- **Chapters 6 through 9** offer detailed case examples and cover some important considerations in treating various diagnoses, including PTSD, chronic pain, depression, and anxiety.

- Finally, **chapter 10** discusses possible directions for the future of tapping and EP.

While there are many moving parts to this method, EP and tapping are actually quite straightforward to learn and apply. It just takes some knowledge and practice. And you don't have to be a psychologist or therapist to be successful with tapping; almost anybody can learn how to do it. However, tapping is not a substitute for training, knowledge, and ethics in areas for which you may apply it.

If you are a therapist or coach, I suggest that you read the entire book, focusing on the applications, and practice on yourself, as well as friends and colleagues, before using it with clients and patients. If you intend to use these techniques for self-help purposes, please be aware that the interventions and modalities covered are best provided with the assistance of a mental health professional or coach who has detailed training and experience in this approach. It's not that you can't be successful in applying tapping for certain problems, but many professionals have found that even they need the help of a fellow professional to resolve their most difficult problems. Joining with someone in this kind of relationship is an invaluable ingredient for success.

So, with that said, let's continue on our tapping and EP journey.

Chapter 1

My Story and the History of Tapping

Whether I shall turn out to be the hero of my own life, or whether that station will be held by anybody else, these pages must show.

—David Copperfield

Similar to you, many of my life experiences have been pretty ordinary, while others were quite amazing, as I recall and write about them now. Generally, we don't report on the ordinary events but, rather, the ones that stand out—and those are the events that define us, for better or for worse.

In my childhood, tragedy struck when I was 11 years old, when my mother was diagnosed with breast cancer and then lymphoma, ending her life at age 43. I was three months shy of 13 when she died. I watched and listened helplessly as my passionate and vibrant mother withered away in agony. You see, in those days, cancer patients mostly remained at home with insufficient pain medication to the bitter end, which meant intense physical and emotional pain. Chemotherapy and other cancer treatments weren't yet available, so she underwent multiple surgeries and radiation treatments that burned both cancer cells and healthy ones.

I remember when my father told me that she was going to die. They had just returned from the hospital, where she was receiving radiation treatment. I was making my brothers' beds and my father entered the room. "I have to tell you something," he said with hesitation in his voice.

I looked at him, thinking that he was going to tell me to do more around the house. "I know," I gasped. "Mom's sick and I need to help out. Can't you see I'm making the beds?"

"No, that's not it. I know you're helping a lot," he said in a solemn tone. "We just saw the doctor. And the doctor said—" he hesitated. "The doctor says that Mommy's going to die."

In that moment, it felt like a surge of electricity coursed through my body. I was overcome by fear and felt the blood rushing out of my face. I was literally shocked. Then I felt numb and weak. Immediately, I dropped to my knees. My entire body felt drained of life energy. And then I slowly rose and walked toward the door, oblivious to anything but the numb feeling and sense of unreality. Any remaining hopes that she might survive were dashed to the ground.

Then my father called to me. I turned and ran toward him, held on to him, and cried. He held me, and after a few minutes, he told me not to let Mom see me crying, that I had to be strong.

She suffered immensely, as did we. She had a little gold-colored bell that she rang when she needed help as she lay in her bed. I remember one evening when I didn't hear the bell as soon as I should have. When I finally heard it and went to see what she needed, she cried that she had been ringing the bell for a long time. I felt tremendously sad and guilty for getting caught up in whatever I was doing at the time and not hearing the bell. She didn't scold me; I did that to myself.

My three brothers and my sister also suffered. However, up until the point of her death, my father and I kept the secret from my siblings that her illness was terminal, which was probably best given their younger ages. And she kept the secret too; she didn't talk to me about her condition and her possible fate either. It wasn't until the day the ambulance took her to the hospital for the final time that I realized that she had known all along. She kissed us children and told us to "be good." As I looked into her eyes, it was clear that we both understood that this would be the last time we would see each other in this life.

For me, my mom's illness and death were both agonizing and numbing. And these traumatic memories interfered with my relationships for many years to come. I had complex grief and tried to cope by not thinking about it, by telling myself that it was long ago, and sometimes by emotionally reliving the painful events that occurred before and after her death. But ultimately none of this seemed to help. Really, I don't think it occurred to me that my pain could be eliminated by anything other than the passage of time, if that. Yet time was not healing the wounds, and I had to wait for close to four decades for relief through other means.

During my mother's illness, I often retreated into fantasy to cope. I spent a lot of time at an old Royal typewriter that my father brought home from his office, writing a variety of novels—each of which I sent to several publishers, only to receive a slew of rejection letters. However, I would go on to publish numerous articles and books on psychology. Apparently, Henry Ford was right when he said, "If you think you can or you think you can't, you're right." My aspiring vision was that I can! This is true of you as well.

I also had an interest in magic, psychology, and hypnosis. I recall that when I was 15 years old, I hypnotized my 10-year-old brother, Philip, and a few neighborhood friends. Of course, I wasn't very proficient at hypnosis at that young age, but my aspiration to understand the human mind was so strong that, after college, I applied to a doctoral program in clinical psychology at Duquesne that would begin the following year. However, since life is often unpredictable, the unpredictable happened. The day after my college graduation, I was in an automobile accident and nearly lost my life.

It was early June 1968, and I was driving my red Volkswagen Beetle to the university's student union to meet friends when a car much larger than mine—I believe it was a Chevy—ripped off my driver's door. This was before seat belts became standard in cars, so the crash sent me flying through the air in what seemed to be slow motion, into some wooden steps that broke under the impact of my body. Then I bounced over a railing, slid along the sidewalk, and rolled over before coming to an abrupt stop. I immediately tried to get up, and at that moment, I could feel that I was bleeding inside. I rolled over and looked up at the sky, terrified that I was going to die. I shouted, "No! I'm not going to die! I'm not ready." I believe my determination, among other forces, was key to my survival.

An ambulance rushed me to Mercy Hospital, just around the corner. I had many injuries, including a ruptured spleen. I underwent surgery and received six pints of blood, with my life hanging in the balance for several days. I was in the intensive care unit for the first four days and in the hospital for ten days altogether. During that time, I was given morphine and developed a dependence on the euphoric sensation that it can give you. Regardless of the temptation, I never turned to morphine again.

For nearly three months after the accident, I recovered at home. Even though my physical condition improved quickly, I continued to experience psychological effects for many years: fear when I was driving, anxiety, flashbacks, and frequent episodes of panic with the feeling that I was going to die. As a result of this trauma—complicated by the previous traumas related to my mother's death—I suffered from PTSD, generalized anxiety, panic disorder, and phobia.

One evening I experienced a particularly severe panic attack that continued for over two hours. I tried everything I could think of to settle the panic: walking around the house wringing my hands, soaking my head in water, taking a warm shower, taking a cold shower, quickly downing a shot of whiskey, breathing deeply into a paper bag, running down the street and back, trying to console myself with rational self-talk, and more. Finally, I became disgusted and angry with the panic and, oddly enough, tried to intensify it. I closed my eyes and focused on the panic sensations—peering into the abyss, so to speak. With defiance, I spoke to the panic, "Come on and get me!"

The curious result was the complete opposite: the panic instantly vanished. I had come face-to-face with my fear and stared it straight in the eye, and in response it dissipated. The satisfaction I felt about this serendipitous discovery! From then on, I no longer lived in dread of panic. If a twinge of anxiety occurred, I faced it, observed it, and tried to intensify it, and it would vanish. Later I learned that what I did was essentially paradoxical intention, a technique that Victor Frankl described in *Man's Search for Meaning* (1946). Although I have found that some people can apply my "come-and-get-me" approach to panic, most people just can't bring themselves to do it. However, combining this attitude with tapping, mindfulness, and an understanding of the autonomic nervous system has been a godsend (as this book will later cover in detail).

After recovering from my injuries and surgeries, it was too late for me to get accepted into Duquesne's graduate program in clinical psychology, so I applied to their graduate philosophy program. I also applied to become an eighth-grade teacher at St. Sebastian school in the Pittsburgh area. I was accepted to both and began teaching and studying in the fall of 1968. However, while reading an inspiring chapter on Heidegger as part of my philosophy coursework, I came to the realization that philosophy was not enough for me. I needed something that was more concrete, something that made it possible to have a visible impact. With philosophy, I thought I would only be able to teach and write about it. I didn't realize at the time the tremendous impact that philosophy has on people's lives and on the field of psychology. Nonetheless, it was becoming clearer that I needed to return to my earlier aspiration.

When the school year ended, I decided not to continue teaching eighth grade and to instead pursue a career in psychology. After several bumps in the road, I was accepted into the clinical psychology program at the University of Dayton, where I earned my MA. I then completed my PhD at the University of Pittsburgh. During this time, I got some exposure to phenomenological psychology and also studied behavioral, gestalt, and experimental approaches. Upon completing my degrees, I worked at various agencies and hospitals, and then ended up working in private practice for some time.

But eventually, I became somewhat antsy. I'm a variety and exploration guy, which I may have inherited from my great-grandfather, Ferdinand, who migrated from Italy and planted roots in America, and my father, who developed skills in music, engineering, refrigeration, and business. I really felt the need for something new and powerful, especially in the treatment of trauma, PTSD, and phobias—and that's when Roger Callahan's tapping method came along. I became so fascinated with this concept and technique that I immersed myself thoroughly in it. I studied closely with Callahan, learned his approach and roots, and in time even developed my own methods.

Although I have found tapping to be superior to many other methods in relieving emotional distress—including in resolving my own traumas—EP has encountered resistance over the years, in part due to the energetic theory behind the approach and its limited research support at first. Early on, Callahan claimed that his approach was effective because it sends kinetic energy, via tapping, into the acupuncture meridian energy system. Additionally, he maintained that there are "perturbations in the thought field" of the psychological problem. That is, psychological problems exist in thought fields, which are energetic fields. However, the distress is a function of the perturbations, which are information markers similar to genetic codes but more closely related to active information. (Active information was proposed by theoretical physicist David Bohm in 1980 to account for the movement of subatomic particles.)

Callahan maintained that the most fundamental basis of a psychological problem is the perturbations that have a one-to-one connection with the tapping points, which are acupoints on the 12 primary meridians and two primary vessels. The tapping results in collapsing or subsuming the perturbations, which in turn neutralizes the distress that fuels the problem. He also recognized that the perturbations cause a subsequent cascade of neurological, chemical, and cognitive effects.

When I first learned about tapping, there was no sound research to support the method. The only preliminary evidence came from two studies of call-in subjects on radio talk shows, who reported significant decreases in their distress level after using the method (Callahan, 1987; Leonoff, 1995). Each of these studies had 68 subjects with various phobic and other anxiety complaints. All told, 132 of the 136 subjects were successfully treated with tapping. This translates into a 97 percent success rate, which is really quite outstanding. However, the studies were replete with methodological problems. For instance, there were no control groups, placebo treatments, double blinds, follow-up evaluations, or evaluative measures other than the subject's subjective distress rating. Furthermore, the investigators were also proponents of tapping, which is a potential source of strong bias.

However, since that time, there have been over 245 peer-reviewed journal articles on acupoint tapping, research studies, and meta-analyses published in professional peer-reviewed journals. This includes 65 randomized controlled trials, 51 clinical outcomes studies, 5 meta-analyses, 17 systematic reviews of various EP modalities, and 9 comparative reviews of EP with other therapies, such as eye movement desensitization and reprocessing (EMDR) and cognitive behavioral therapy (CBT; Feinstein, 2021). All but one of the experimental studies have documented the effectiveness of EP in treating physical pain, anxiety, depression, cravings, trauma, and PTSD, as well as supporting peak athletic performance. Of the meta-analyses, one revealed a moderate effect size (Gilomen & Lee, 2015), while four others showed large effect sizes (Church et al., 2020; Clond, 2016; Nelms & Castel, 2016; Sebastian & Nelms, 2017).

My colleagues and I have similarly treated thousands of clients suffering from intense traumas, PTSD, and other emotionally charged disorders. We have found that tapping allows us to achieve generally efficient results without the client having to experience distress during the process. You might say that therapist enthusiasm is another active ingredient in this treatment. Although there is no question in my mind that the quality of the therapist-client relationship is a major factor in any effective therapy, I've never found enthusiasm to be the sufficient condition for therapeutic success.

You can find more up-to-date research on EP in the research section of the Association for Comprehensive Energy Psychology (ACEP) website (www.energypsych.org), as well as in the readings section of my website (www.energypsych.com). You can also check out the appendix in this book for a list of recommended readings and resources.

Now let's turn to issues of preparation.

Chapter 2

Preparation, Assumptions, and the RILITA Model

We keep moving forward, opening up new doors and doing new things, because we're curious... and curiosity keeps leading us down new paths.

—Walt Disney

There is a tale about William James, who was a leading philosopher and psychologist in the late nineteenth century and is considered the founder of American psychology. While lecturing on the role of assumptions in science, James emphasized that our presuppositions, upon which knowledge is based, rest upon little more than faith. Underneath the assumption is nothing other than our faith in the assumption. As an illustration, he offered the example of the planets revolving around the sun, noting that they are supported by nothing other than our assumptions or theories about something called gravity, which we obviously cannot see but instead infer.

When the lecture was over, an elderly gentleman approached James, expressing enthusiasm about the presentation but also begging to disagree about the orbiting planets. He insisted that the planets actually rest on the backs of giant tortoises that walk around the sun along the paths we call orbits.

In an effort to enlighten the gentleman further about the true purpose of the planet analogy, James simply inquired as to what might be supporting the tortoises as they make their trek around the sun, suggesting that at the bottom they were supported by nothing.

To this the old man quickly and adamantly replied, "Oh, no, sir! You ain't gonna get me on that one. It's turtles all the way down!"

But, of course, it can't be "turtles all the way down." At some point, you run out of turtles—where there's nothing underneath, where our assumptions become blatantly obvious. Even assumptions that have considerable rational, intuitive, or clinical support are still assumptions, and they merely represent the foundation upon which a structure is built. All structures eventually topple, more or less, as their foundations can only support so much.

For example, in the area of physics, Newtonian laws make accurate predictions within a limited area but require adjustments when making predictions concerning subatomic particles (or are they waves?), velocities approaching the speed of light (assumed to be the ultimate speed), travel between point A and point B (or is it all of a sudden according to quantum physics?), and so on. In everyday life, it's likely that you have experienced this truth, where you thought things were one way and then were struck by evidence to the contrary and had to change your thinking and perception. You should always be open to adjusting your lens when the facts call for it.

Practical Assumptions

To reiterate, an important aspect of any model is the assumptions or beliefs upon which it is based. Before going into the details of the therapeutic model covered here, let's look at our assumptions.

Mental health is innate. Healthy psychological functioning is potentially available to everyone. Not all therapies are based on this assumption; the client is often seen as pathologic and the therapist's objective is to offer support to the client in some respect. However, we are assuming that regardless of the apparent pathology, the client is, in their essence, healthy and has plenty of wisdom. By holding this view—and I mean really holding it in your heart and mind—it becomes possible to draw out the health in the client.

It may well be that the first step is to meet the client where they are; otherwise, they will feel that you don't recognize the seriousness of their predicament. However, it is very important to not get caught up in the surface problem, since that will lower your spirits as a therapist and seal in the pathology for the client. To paraphrase Henry Ford, if you think they're healthy or you think they're not, you're right. This is also consistent with what I refer to as the *Michelangelo principle*, since that Renaissance artist perceived the figure embedded in the stone and helped to free it from its prison. Here you are helping actualize the client's health, which is always already there.

We create our realities through the principles of energy, mind, thought, and consciousness. These principles are informed in part by the work of Sidney Banks (1998) and his followers. The essential principles by which you create your experiential reality are not limited to external factors. You have *mind*, which is the context or vehicle through which you create thought. This is beyond your brain, as your mind infuses your whole being. Mind takes two forms: the universal mind and your personal mind. Universal mind pervades the universe. It's in animals, plants, planets, stars—everything. Personal mind is individual and subjective.

Next comes *thought*. Thought is not real in a physical sense, although it is "real thought." It has been proposed that thought is a function of neurons firing and chemical reactions, but thought is more than that. To reduce thought to the firing of neurons or chemical reactions is extremely reductionistic. Thought makes it possible to create. And thought manifests in words, images, internal smells and tastes, and feelings. Feelings are essentially felt thoughts. Thinking is pervasive and can involve *processing thinking* as well as *inspirational* or *receiver-mode thinking*.

This brings us to another aspect of your experiential reality: *consciousness*. It is through consciousness that you are able to experience reality. Consciousness also allows you to experience memories or imaginings—you can have a thought about something and feel as if it's real, even when it's not. Depending on your level of understanding, which is another aspect of consciousness, you can step beyond specific thoughts (i.e., step outside of them) and understand that these are thoughts and that you are the thinker. All of this—mind, thought, and consciousness—is essentially energy in different forms.

Bioenergy and feelings resonate from one person to another. The health of the therapist resonates with and impacts the client. If your energy—meaning your mind, thoughts, and consciousness—is at a healthy level, this will affect the client. And this will support the client in moving to a state of health, and you in drawing out the health within the client. This is essentially a resonance principle that is consistent with cybernetic theory: The element within the system that has the highest vibration will affect or control the system.

I'm reminded of the Dutch physicist and inventor of the pendulum clock, Christaan Huygens, who discovered that independent pendulum clocks in a specific location will synchronize to one another. In time, it was discovered that the other clocks synchronize to the clock with the strongest spring, the strongest vibration. This same principle applies to therapy and other communication endeavors. If the therapist is in a state of health—or a high state of vibration, in physics terms—this will impact the client in a positive way. It also works in reverse: If the negative state is the most powerful, you'll synchronize to it. You've likely had the experience of being around someone who was in a highly positive or negative state, and this affected the way you felt.

Feeling secure facilitates learning and mental health. Therapy is not conducted well when the client or the therapist is in a state of insecurity. Old-style therapy, which may still be practiced in some circles, would encourage the client to let it all hang out, to really get into the distress that they've been experiencing, to review the traumatic experiences of their lives. I used to do that. I believed that I wasn't doing my job if the client wasn't powerfully emoting. But pushing your client to emote disrupts their energy and can create a profound feeling of insecurity. It's very difficult for the client to benefit and learn when they're in such a state.

From a neurological standpoint, when we're distressed, we're in fight-flight-or-freeze mode. That's a state of insecurity, an experience of danger, that interferes with our ability to think clearly. So wallowing in distress is not the answer. Many clients are already accomplished at doing that, and they've come to you hoping to get out of such a disruptive pattern. Perhaps it is beneficial for them to tune into a distressing thought, memory, or emotional state, but it is important to simultaneously equip them with the ability to step back and neutralize the distressing emotional state so they can achieve a state of peace and access their wisdom. Higher levels of consciousness make this possible, and the techniques and understandings covered in this book will make it possible for your clients to achieve such a secure state.

Therapists who follow their own leanings have the greatest therapeutic impact. It's best to conduct therapy in your own personal style. While it's fine to be influenced by therapeutic and communication masters, your approach won't be as congruent or powerful if you try to do therapy in exactly their way. You cannot be somebody other than yourself in the therapeutic context (or in any context, for that matter). Your power lies in being real and being in the moment with your client. So it's not a matter of "the" way, but "my way" or "your way." I think this is a function of the interaction and relationship between a specific client and a specific therapist. For example, the same client will have a distinct relationship with you compared to another therapist.

The client's problem is a reflection of limited understanding and energetic disruption. Elevating understanding and removing energetic blocks changes the problem. For example, if a client is distressed when recalling an upsetting event, it is generative for the client to come to understand in a deep sense that the distress is a function of their thoughts, which may include images, words, sounds, and feelings associated with the memory. However, very often the emotional impact is so strong that it is difficult, if not impossible, to step back and realize that the distress is an echo from the past.

Therefore, there are many energetic techniques that help reduce the emotional impact of the memory and make it possible to have this higher level of understanding. While dissipating emotional distress is certainly beneficial, when clients realize that distress is a function of thought (thought recognition), and not solely because of their circumstances, it helps seal in the results of our techniques and empowers the client.

The ability to realize thought in the moment as the source of your experiential reality provides a sense of well-being. An age-old concept in psychotherapy is internal locus of control versus external locus of control. If you experience your situation from an external locus of control perspective, you will feel vulnerable and powerless. While there are many things that are indeed beyond your control, your psychological state or subjective experience can be seen as entirely within your control. And once you understand that your experience is a function of your thoughts and not solely a result of the external situation, you no longer feel vulnerable.

An important goal of therapy is to transition the client's worldview from an external to an internal locus of control. When you enhance the client's awareness of thought as the fundamental source of their distress (i.e., thought recognition) and equip them with efficient techniques to dissipate their distress, the client will feel—and be—less vulnerable to external or past circumstances. This affords ready access to their mental health.

Our teaching and energetic treatments should be specifically focused in the areas of relevance to the client. The more specific the treatment, the more effective. To simply offer a philosophical position can be interesting, but it is usually not sufficient to promote profound change. For example, if a client asks for help with anxiety, targeting specific worries, one at a time, is more effective than attempting to address anxiety in general. And in overcoming one specific anxiety response, the client learns how to deal with anxiety in other situations. However, it can also be useful and effective to have the client attune to the sensations of anxiety in the moment—mindfully describing what it feels like in the body—and recognize the thoughts at the core of the anxiety, while simultaneously dissipating the anxiety sensations via an EP technique such as tapping.

It is best to teach clients how to listen better, clear their minds, and energetically treat themselves. While there are exceptions to the rule, many people don't listen very well. They may be so caught up in their distress, their internal processing, and their distracting thoughts that they are not able to hear what you are offering them. The same consideration applies to the therapist; it is of utmost importance to be able to listen, with little or nothing else in your mind.

Discussing this with your client can elevate their ability to listen and absorb what is being offered (and remind you to do the same). You can usually tell when the client is not listening well, and the skill of listening can be discussed at these opportune moments. Also, when explaining and guiding a client through an energetic technique such as tapping, it is again important that they listen well so they can use the technique effectively.

Therapy is best done as teamwork. Clients often come to therapy with the belief that the therapist will fix them. The therapist is the authority in their view. (This is another example of external locus of control.) While the initial pace in therapy may be to accept this position that the client holds, it is important as soon as possible to make it clear that therapy is teamwork. It is true that the therapist is equipped with theoretical understandings and practical skills.

However, the client must assume responsibility for learning and applying the skills that the therapist has to offer. If this is not an essential aspect of therapy, it is unlikely that the work will be effective.

The RILITA Model

Inspired by the work of Carl Rogers (1951), Sidney Banks (1998, 2001), and George Pransky (1992), I have developed a very practical model that I use in my work. I refer to it as the RILITA model. The acronym stands for six different aspects of a conversational process that can be used with tapping, as well as in other therapy and communication endeavors.

The first step involves **rapport**, which pervades the entire interaction. Next is **inquiry**, in which you ask questions to find out why the client has come to you. As you ask your questions, you **listen** in a very special way to the client and ask follow-up questions. Out of this type of listening, combined with your inquiry and rapport, an **inspiration** will occur, which may lead to other questions for further clarification.

At some point, it becomes very clear what the client needs, and at this point you **teach** this understanding to the client via any number of techniques that you have available. When you hit the mark, a change will occur in the client. You may see the change in the moment or detect it in a follow-up visit. If no change occurs, you will need to make **adjustments** (for example, focusing on reestablishing rapport if it was lost). When you pay attention to the process itself, including identifying and resolving any issues, you make it that much more likely to succeed.

Let's explore each step of the RILITA model in greater detail.

Rapport

Even if you have a lot of techniques in your toolbox—such as tapping, using visualization exercises, or challenging limiting thoughts and beliefs—if you do something like that at the very first session, the client may not return. That's because the therapeutic process first and foremost involves a relationship: the relationship between the therapist and the client. And this kind of relationship is unique. It can be a friendship of sorts, but it's also quite different, since it's a professional relationship with ethical issues involved.

The therapeutic relationship is based upon a deep acceptance of the client and a deep sense of rapport, which is referred to as unconditional positive regard (Rogers, 1951). Therefore, rapport is the first order of business, and it's most important that you, as the therapist, are competent and that your competency is visible to the client. You also need to believe and recognize that there is more to the client than what meets the eye. As you interact with this person, you congruently and honestly welcome opportunities to elevate them and to acknowledge their strengths and achievements.

Preferably you have a good feeling about the client and you don't hold negative judgments about them. But if any negative or distracting thoughts do arise, you don't get wrapped up in them. Instead, you maintain a sense of mindfulness by nonjudgmentally observing your thoughts and dropping any negative or distracting thoughts that pop up, rather than getting caught up in them. As a result of this, your energy remains balanced and this energetically touches the client, which brings out the health in the client.

Inquiry and Listening

Once you have established rapport, it's time to ask your client some pertinent questions. You inquire about what they want from therapy or coaching: "I read over your intake form, where you described some of the problems you've been experiencing. How can I help you? What brings you here today? What can I do for you? What can we (*together*) do for you?"

Then you listen to your client. And you listen and observe in a very special way, with basically nothing on your mind. Perhaps you listen in the way that you would listen to music, the sounds of a stream, or the sounds of cars passing by. You don't listen to make a diagnosis or to confirm a theory. Instead, you listen for a relevant blind spot in the client's level of understanding. In a sense, you come from a beginner's mind. Rather than automatically filling in the blanks, you allow yourself to be puzzled and curious, which will lead you to the core of what you need to understand and what the client needs to understand. This way of thinking is a lot like that of Lieutenant Colombo, Mr. Monk, or

DCI Barnaby. You follow your puzzlement, and this leads you and the client organically to what you need to know and what you need to do.

Inquiry also involves asking questions in a respectful manner; it's not an interrogation. The therapist or coach functions as an anthropologist of sorts, who is observing and seeking to understand a unique culture. You ask questions to usher in a deeper understanding of what is going on with the client for the sake of the client. You don't try to remember what the client just said or did, since this can get in the way of listening and observing in the moment. You simply allow yourself to be touched by what the client says and does. It's best to teach the client to do this as well. The better you and the client listen, the greater the chances of positive results. By listening in this way, you are open to receiving inspiration.

Inspiration

What the client needs to understand will occur to both you and your client as you listen and observe. The realization occurs out of the blue—an aha moment! It isn't the result of analysis or a theory about how things are. It's a realization in the moment that perhaps comes from universal consciousness. In some ways, this is like when you're trying to remember the name of a song you heard. You struggle to retrieve it. And the harder you try, the more stress you feel and the more evasive the answer becomes. When you stop struggling and give yourself a chance to step back and let go of trying to figure it out, you enter the field of inspiration. It's a different kind of mental process—the process whereby creativity occurs. An integral aspect of this inspiration is the belief that everything is fixable. Beliefs either stop you in your tracks or propel you forward and beyond.

I've heard it said that when Einstein was struggling to come up with a solution to a theoretical issue, he had to be very careful when he was shaving. When he was paying attention to shaving instead of whatever issue he was struggling with, it was during those moments that the answer would arrive. It could be so shocking that he might even cut himself. Indeed, some of our most creative moments occur during times like these, whether we're taking a shower or bath, relaxing on vacation, listening to music, mowing the grass, or maybe even cutting out paper dolls. This is a commonsense understanding that we all have the ability to apply. It's about stepping outside of the box.

Teaching

After your inspiration occurs, you check it out with the client to see if it fits. This gives you information about the client's level of understanding. When the time is ripe, you then teach the client using examples, constructs, metaphors, techniques, assignments, and so on. It is important for the learning to be relevant to the client's particular circumstances, such that it is informed by the client's blind spots. It is also important for the client to really want to learn about what you have to teach them, so you need to have a type of pact with the client about learning in the targeted area. If you maintain a clear mind during this process, the issue will resonate with you and your client, and your minds will tune into higher knowing.

Adjustments

After offering an intervention, observe the client to determine whether a result has occurred. You'll be able to tell if this has happened, since the client will change. The trauma will no longer bother them, the feeling of depression will dissipate, the physical pain will be relieved, or they will lighten up in some other way. Sometimes the change will not be evident until you see the client at a follow-up session. If no change occurs, adjustments are needed. And the teaching-learning process continues.

Adjustments can occur at many levels: using a different metaphor, construct, or therapeutic exercise; reestablishing rapport; improving the client's listening (or your own); reevaluating what you are trying to teach; or whatever else is relevant in the moment. Sometimes your adjustment comes from the realization that you were caught up in your own ego, overly invested in a theory, or trying to do something that is not real for you. However, never fail to believe that change is possible and even inevitable—that the health within the client is already there and accessible.

It may be that the client has not come to see you to achieve a change, in which case that becomes an important aspect of the adjustment as well. Some clients simply come to therapy to talk, to be understood, or to be agreed with, in which case a different level of adjustment may be needed. Depending on your inclination as a therapist or coach, adjustments may involve agreeing to continue with simply listening and confirming, asking pertinent questions, and assisting the client to focus on making changes that can improve the quality of their life, or perhaps simply agreeing to a friendly parting of ways.

Next Step

Now that we've outlined the RILITA model, it's time to move on to some techniques that many of my colleagues and I have found to be highly effective in helping dissipate unwanted emotional reactions, change core beliefs, relieve physical pain, treat PTSD and other forms of trauma, relieve phobias and depression, enhance peak performance, and more. The next chapter focuses on tapping and ancillary techniques in their various forms. Always keep in mind, though, that the true change isn't from the tapping itself but from tapping into the client's real power. Here's where the rubber meets the road. Enjoy the journey.

Chapter 3

How to Tap

When the wolf's at the door… just tap your troubles away.
—Mack and Mabel

The Case of Barbara

In 1993, I had the opportunity to see Barbara, a 33-year-old patient whom I had treated previously. While the earlier treatment was of some benefit to her, there was an event that occurred in her childhood for which I was not able to help. That event was a sexual assault. She was 13 at the time and a 19-year-old forced himself on her. She never told her parents about it but suffered silently. She experienced frequent nightmares, turned to drugs and alcohol, overate, and was extremely depressed. She believed she was not worthwhile and even blamed herself.

When Barbara returned to see me, she was upset about a recent argument with her mother. This was causing her to recall a number of distressing memories concerning their relationship. After listening to her concerns, I explained that I had been doing a new form of therapy that involved tapping on specific points on the body to relieve problems. I suggested that we do this for her, and she was agreeable. Within a few minutes of her tapping at specific locations, she was no longer distressed about her mother. She felt more positive and hopeful about their relationship. She even stated that she didn't understand why it had bothered her so much, since that is simply the way her mother is and she means well.

Next, I asked Barbara if it would be okay to treat the trauma that happened to her when she was 13. Immediately, she began to cry as she recalled the event.

To help her focus away from the distressing memories and bodily sensations that were occupying her in the moment, I directed her to look at and describe various objects in the office: the lamp, the table, knickknacks. This helped her to shift her state and feel relatively more secure, and to be more present.

With her permission, I then guided her to tap various points on her body: between her eyebrows, under her eyes and collarbones, on the center of her chest, beneath an armpit, on the edges of certain fingernails, and the like. At times, she started to dissociate, and I called her back and helped her with the tapping. Within a few minutes of this treatment, I observed a miraculous transformation in Barbara. All signs of distress were erased from her face, and her general demeanor was now calm and serene. She reached over to my desk and took a tissue to dry the tears from her face. Then she sat calmly, looking at me with a relaxed, peaceful expression. It is an understatement to say that I was amazed at what I was witnessing.

Not very successfully concealing my astonishment, I asked Barbara, "How do you feel?"

Her response was a simple, nonchalant "fine"—as if to say, "Why do you ask?"

"I mean, about what happened to you when you were 13?" I asked.

"It's just something that happened to me when I was a kid," she said calmly.

"But you were raped!" I exclaimed. "Doesn't that bother you now?"

Barbara shook her head and simply said, "No, it doesn't."

I wanted to test the stability of this amazing change. Earlier she had cried that she was to blame and that she hadn't listened to her mother, so—as difficult as it was to ask this—I inquired if Barbara still thought the assault was her fault.

"No," she said, unshaken and congruently. "I wasn't to blame. If anything, he was. But that's in the past now."

I was dumbfounded. I had never seen such a remarkable change occur in such a short period of time—practically immediate! You'd think that Barbara would have been flabbergasted as well, but she was nonchalant. Maybe even unimpressed, as if nothing had happened!

I saw Barbara several times at follow-ups. That trauma never bothered her after that brief treatment. All the talking we had done previously, all the visualizations, all the attempts at getting her to think more "rationally" about the trauma, all the emoting—none of it did anything compared to a few minutes of tapping, which quickly changed how she felt and thought about the sexual assault and about herself.

I continued to offer treatment to Barbara over the course of several months, talking and tapping for other accumulated issues in her life with efficient results. She stopped drinking and using drugs, her depression and anxiety dissipated, and she found renewed purpose in her life. She went on to college and graduate school, and she eventually became a licensed social worker and psychotherapist. Our relationship and the resolution of that early trauma loosened things up for her in a really big way. And I must say that this really helped me, as well, as I set out on an inspiring mission that transformed my own life.

The Body's Energy System

The therapy I provided to Barbara—and to thousands of other clients over the last several decades—is based on the idea that the body has an energy system that follows pathways referred to as meridians. These meridians interact with a number of more concentrated energy centers called chakras, as well as with detectable energy fields around the body. And if energy really does saturate every cubic centimeter of space throughout the universe, as physicists David Bohm and Basil J. Hiley elucidated (Bohm, 1980; Bohm & Hiley, 1993), then the meridians are part and parcel of our connections to each other—and to everything else, for that matter.

In order to effectively use specific tapping techniques (which we will get to shortly), you first need to understand this energy system. So let's consider some facts about acupuncture and tapping. This information will also be helpful to you in explaining the basis of tapping techniques to your clients.

Acupuncture and Meridians

About 5,000 years ago, individuals in China discovered that the body has an energy system that follows pathways called *meridians*. Predating the Chinese findings by a couple thousand years, the same bioenergy system was elucidated in India. There is also evidence that similar knowledge sprung up long ago in other parts of the world, including Egypt and Brazil, as well as among the Bantu peoples of Africa and the indigenous tribes of North America (Chang, 1976; Walther, 1988).

The Chinese system detailed 12 primary bilateral meridians, each of which passes through a specific organ in the body—including the lungs, heart, stomach, and liver—in addition to collector meridians, which intersect the front and back of the body and enter the brain. There are also a number of collateral pathways that interconnect with the primary meridians. The entire system is interconnected with a flow of energy called *qi* or *chi* (pronounced "chee"). Qi appears to be electromagnetic and subtle energy.

How the meridians were discovered remains a mystery. Theories abound: Some have suggested that it was uncovered via trial and error, while others maintain it was tracked down due to the positive health benefits of injuries to specific bodily locations. It has even been suggested that the individuals who discovered the meridian system possessed higher sensory abilities and could see, hear, and palpate the flow within the meridians; as a result, they were able to map out the meridian topography. Today, while many acupuncturists apply specific protocols or recipes for needle placement, other, more highly skilled acupuncturists are able to detect flow of qi by palpating pulses on the patient's wrists.

Regardless of how the discoveries were made, the information eventually appeared in the *Nei Ching*, the oldest writing on acupuncture, attributed to Huang Ti, the "Yellow Emperor," who supposedly ruled China for a hundred years (from about 2697 BC to 2597 BC). Modern-day acupuncture has deviated little from this text, suggesting that the system was developed and refined over the course of many preceding centuries.

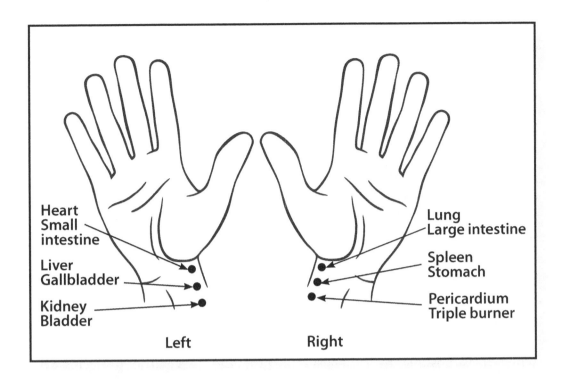

Heart
Small
intestine

Liver
Gallbladder

Kidney
Bladder

Lung
Large intestine

Spleen
Stomach

Pericardium
Triple burner

Left   **Right**

Acupoint Stimulation and Applied Kinesiology

Although acupuncture is done with needles, acupoints can be stimulated in other ways, so it is better referred to as meridian therapy. Other forms of stimulation include pressure, rubbing, running one's hands in the direction of the meridian flow, suction cups, herbs, vitamins, minerals, glandular extracts, specialized exercises, manipulation of specific muscles, burning moxa* (moxibustion), and—as you may have deduced—tapping!

George Goodheart, the founder of applied kinesiology, explored the effectiveness of tapping or percussing at specific acupoints to alleviate physical pain. To determine where the tapping should be applied, Goodheart employed muscle testing and therapy localization. This method involves having the patient touch specific locations on their body while the practitioner tests the relative strength of an isolated muscle, also called an indicator muscle.

Later, Roger Callahan found that tapping on certain acupoints is beneficial in treating a wide range of psychological problems. Recall his treatment of Mary,

* Moxa is made from ground leaves of Eurasian artemisia and is used in the form of sticks or cones that are kindled and put on acupoints or used to heat acupuncture needles.

who had a severe water phobia. This is similar to the way in which I successfully treated Barbara. Many of us have found that it is possible to treat a variety of intractable problems by having the client tap on specific acupoints while tuning into their emotional issue, physical pain, or limiting beliefs.

Needless to say, this approach to therapy does not fit neatly into usual ways of thinking about change. Many professionals maintain that the way to treat psychological and emotional problems is by changing environmental and life circumstances, changing thoughts, or altering neurochemistry. There is no obviously convincing basis for believing that tapping on the body while thinking about a problem can cause a dramatic change to occur. In scientific terms, tapping seems to lack face validity—that is, it doesn't look like it could possibly be valid. Many people would think that tapping could only work by distraction or via a placebo effect. However, distraction commonly results in only temporary relief, and placebos are effective only about a third of the time.

While it is possible to treat psychological and psychiatric problems with environmental, cognitive, and chemical means, generally such approaches do not produce rapid, profound changes. They work over time and often result in improvement, but not total elimination of the problem. Frequently, treatment must be ongoing, and the patient is seldom considered to be cured. I believe that this is due, in part, to the fact that these approaches do not specifically address the energy system that governs emotional responses. That is, when a negative emotion occurs, it is triggered by a change in the energy system, which is the initial domino that sets the whole emotional process in motion. It is not that the circumstances, thoughts, neurons, and chemistry are irrelevant—they are also intricately involved in the issue. While making adjustments at these levels is a useful and often necessary aspect of treatment, when treating specifically at the energy level, you are essentially turning off the switch that stimulates the cascade leading to the negative emotions that hold the problem in place.

Proof of Qi and Meridians

If we could prove that the bodily energy system or qi exists, perhaps this therapy would be more acceptable on an energetic basis. In an effort to investigate qi, some researchers have reportedly photographed the meridians by using radioactive isotopes, although others have searched similarly in vain (de Vernejoul et al., 1984, 1985). But another line of investigation may have proven more fruitful.

Orthopedic surgeon and researcher Robert O. Becker conducted research supporting the existence of a primitive bodily energy system that also accounts for the effectiveness of acupuncture. He provided convincing evidence that the *current of injury* that occurs at injury sites is not merely a byproduct of injured cells, but is consistent with a primitive energy-control system that directs regeneration. He found that the direct current (DC) at the site of injury on frogs, which are not highly regenerative, is positively charged, whereas the current on salamanders, for which regeneration is paramount, is negatively charged (Becker, 1990; Becker & Selden, 1985). Similarly, Louis Langman, when examining a sample of women with cervical cancer, found that 96 percent had a negative DC charge in the cervix (the remaining 4 percent had a positive charge). A sample of women with no gynecological conditions showed the reverse pattern, indicating that polarity seems to make a major difference (Langman, 1972).

Becker also offered research supporting the specificity of acupoints and the existence of meridians. In the early 1970s, research into acupuncture was encouraged by the National Institute of Health after President Nixon's visit to China serendipitously brought acupuncture into research vogue when journalist James Reston was effectively treated with acupuncture for postoperative pain. Although many initial investigators thought that acupuncture produced only a placebo effect and that needle placement was irrelevant, Becker approached the problem differently.

He figured that the meridians were electrical conductors that carried messages back and forth between the brain and the injury site, promoting healing while producing a pain message at the same time. He suggested that the purpose of the acupoints was to serve as boosters of the current, similar to the way transformers boost the current along power lines. And, indeed, he detected differences in electrical resistance at the acupoints compared to the surrounding skin, as well as variations on the surface of the skin in the locations of meridians that were distinct from non-meridian skin. Thus, his work points to the reality of the meridians (Becker & Selden, 1985; Reichmanis et al., 1975).

Tapping Techniques

Now that you understand the history and research behind tapping, you're ready to start learning specific tapping techniques. Here's a basic rundown of how to achieve results similar to what occurred for Mary, Barbara, and other cases discussed throughout this book.

Tuning In

After establishing rapport, inquiring, and listening (the first three steps of the RILITA model), maybe you get an inspiration that tapping is the way to treat this person's concern. If so, you explain to the client that you're going to do some tapping, which has been found to help. Different people require different amounts of information about the approach. Some want detailed information, while others don't need much explanation at all: "That's okay, Doc. I trust you."

After introducing the treatment and getting the client's agreement to proceed, the next step is to ask the client to tune into or think about the issue to be treated, also referred to as *attunement*. This also applies to self-treatment. For example, let's say you feel upset about a particular situation, or you have a phobia, or you worry a lot. Whatever the issue may be, the first step is to bring to mind the issue as specifically as possible and get in touch with the associated feelings. This activates the energetic and neural circuitry involved in the problem, essentially bringing it online. For example, if you have arachnophobia, you could form a mental image of a spider and focus on how you feel in response to seeing this spider in your mind's eye. However, it's not necessary to wallow in emotional distress. Get just a sample or smidgen, not a population explosion.

Being Specific

It's important to be as specific as possible when tuning in. For example, if you hold a limiting belief that you are unworthy or not good enough, you can tune into the somatic sensations that go along with this belief. Perhaps you experience a feeling of tension in the stomach along with a feeling of being small. Tapping on these sensations may dissipate them, as well as the associated thoughts and beliefs.

It may be necessary to track down specific seminal events that form the basis of the client's limiting belief through what is known as *affect bridging*. A belief is a generalization that developed from one or more specific experiences. Ask the client to take the feeling and to recall the first time or times that they felt this way. What was going on? Even if there were many such events, there might be one highly representative event that they can focus on. By targeting the specific event or events, you can neutralize and transform the overriding limiting belief.

For example, one client came to see me because she would back away from any relationship with a man if he got "too close." She talked about a man she was currently interested in but was about to stop seeing due to this fear of intimacy. I asked her what she was feeling in her body, and she reported feeling tense and shaky. I explained that this feeling likely went back to an earlier relationship, perhaps in her family and during her childhood, and asked her to recall when she first remembered feeling this way. After thinking about it for a few moments, she said that her father was verbally and physically abusive.

I asked her to recall a specific event when he was abusive, upon which she began crying as she described an event from age 5 when she was pushing her baby brother in a buggy that tipped over. The baby cried but was not seriously hurt. Her father hit her, called her names, and sent her to her room. We tapped on this event until she felt better. When she returned the following week, she said, "In 45 minutes you helped me get rid of nearly 30 years of shit!" None of the abusive events from her father bothered her anymore. "Because I think they were all so similar!" she exclaimed. She was also now feeling closer and more secure in her romantic relationship.

This generalization principle also applies to other problems, such as depression or anxiety. In the case of depression, it could be based on a number of events that hold the depression in place. As you tune into and tap on each of those specifics, the depression edifice comes toppling down.

Measurement

Since you now have something tuned in, you might as well take its "temperature" to get a measurement of sorts. This isn't absolutely necessary, but it can be useful. Measuring gives you a basis for determining whether or not the tapping technique is helping. To do so, you ask the client to rate their level of distress on a 0–10 scale, which we call their subjective unit of distress (SUD). For instance, you would ask the arachnophobic client to imagine those crawly little spiders in detail and to rate how much it bothers them. Maybe in this case the client says, "I'm at a 10." That number is your baseline measure of how much distress the client is having about *this* particular issue at *this* point in time. As you proceed with the tapping, periodically ask your client to rate their distress again. If the technique is working, the SUD rating will come down. If it's not working, there will be no change in the number, or it might even increase. Those are important pieces of information.

Some people may not be able to relate to the SUD scale without an image to go along with the number. This especially applies to children. Following is a useful measurement image.

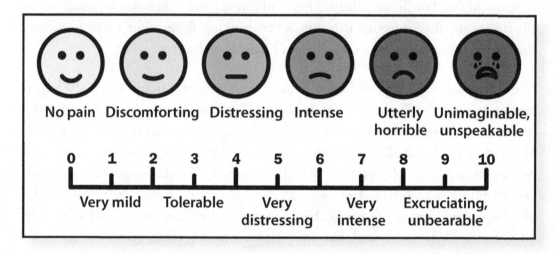

Muscle Testing

It's also possible to use muscle testing to further evaluate the SUD rating. We won't go into muscle testing in great detail in this book, since it's a rather complex procedure that takes considerable experience to develop skill with. But at the most basic level, you test the strength of a muscle—perhaps a shoulder muscle, such as the middle deltoid muscle—by having the client extend their arm off to the side and parallel to the floor. You then apply a little pressure above the client's wrist on the arm while asking the client to meet your pressure. With the muscle now testing strong, ask the client to bring to mind the specific problem, such as a fear of heights. At this point, you again press on the arm with the same intensity you used to test the muscle initially.

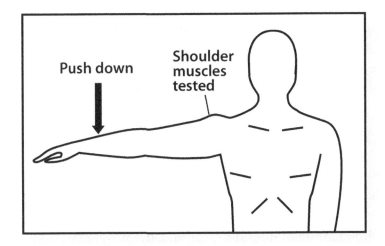

In most cases, there will be a detectable difference in the strength of the muscle. Essentially, the muscle tests weaker. (Though it is not really that the muscle is being *strong* or *weak*, but rather that it's being turned *on* or *off*.) After this test has been conducted, apply the tapping treatment. When the client feels better about the situation—for example, they're no longer bothered by heights—the muscle will now test strong (on), as it was before the process began. There are many other ways to use muscle testing. It can help you determine where it's best to tap, what emotions are involved, the time frame in which a problem began, or if there's some sort of a blockage to improvement, for example. If you want to learn more about muscle testing, consider reading *Energy Diagnostic and Treatment Methods* (Gallo, 2000).

Psychological Reversal

After tuning in and having the client rate their SUD level, it's often necessary to treat a kind of blockage that is referred to by different names, including psychological reversal, psychoenergetic reversal, or simply reversal. Psychological reversal occurs when your actions or motivation are in the opposite direction of your desired goal. It's like walking backward when you intend to go forward. For example, a healthy choice might be to quit smoking, yet a person who is reversed will continue to smoke in spite of their insistence that they want to quit. But reversal doesn't only apply to compulsion and addiction; it is potentially an aspect of any psychological problem. If a client's anxiety, depression, trauma, or any other concern does not decrease with an effective treatment like tapping, one possibility is that they are reversed.

This reversal is another kind of problem that is intertwined with or in front of the specific issue being treated. Essentially, no effective treatment, including tapping, will work when the client is reversed. Therefore, you must first disengage the reversal. If you use muscle testing, you can use it to quickly determine if there is a reversal. But that is not always necessary. You can simply assume that there is a reversal and treat accordingly. Treating for a reversal that doesn't exist won't cause one to emerge, so just go ahead and do it.

How do you correct or disengage reversal? At the most basic level, you simply have the client steadily tap on the little-finger side of their hand while saying three times, "Even though I [*state the problem*], I accept myself." For example, "Even though I'm afraid of dogs, I accept myself." Why make the statement three times? This is what Roger Callahan did in the beginning, and out of deference to him, many of us who have studied with him continue in the same fashion. However, I have often found that it can be sufficient to have the client make the statement one time, especially if they sound and appear highly congruent. Still, it may be useful to have them say it several times to reinforce the statement.

And why tap on the side of the hand? The side of the hand stimulates a specific meridian point, meridian (SI-3), which is the third point on the small intestine. Callahan discovered many years ago that this point is often intricately associated with reversal. There are other points that are effective in treating different kinds of reversals, but tapping on this point will prove sufficient most of the time, as it is useful for a variety of reversals. (I'll go into detail about the other options in chapter 5.)

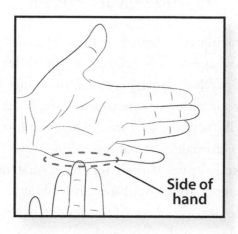

Side of hand

Reversal Correction Statements

There are a variety of statements that can be used in treating psychological reversals. Here are a few examples:

Even though I [*state the problem*]...

- I accept myself.

- I deeply and completely accept myself.

- I deeply and completely love and accept myself.

- I'm okay.

- I'm a good person.

- I'm awesome.

- I deeply accept myself, and I'm open to a miracle.

- I accept myself, and I am safe and secure.

I invite you to use your creativity to devise other statements. For the most part, there are no rigid rules here. However, as much as possible, the statement should include an acknowledgment of the problem and some sort of self-acceptance statement. You may also add another statement directed toward a positive solution. The basic formula looks like this: *Even though X, I accept myself, and I choose Y.* For example:

Even though I [*state the problem*]...

- I'm cool, and I choose to feel safe and secure.

- I accept myself, and I choose to feel better.

- I deeply accept myself, and I choose to be resolved.

- I'm okay, and I choose to feel worthwhile.

- I accept myself, and I choose to feel hopeful and positive.

In my experience, another useful variation to the reversal correction takes into account one of the principles of mindfulness. To say "even though I have this problem" is a judgment of sorts. To eliminate this judgment, you can start off the statement with self-acceptance instead. For example:

- I deeply accept myself with this anxiety, and I accept this anxiety.

- I deeply and completely accept myself with cravings for potato chips.

- I deeply accept myself with these feelings of depression, and I choose to be hopeful.

- I accept myself and these anxiety sensations, and I choose to feel calm and secure.

However, some people have a very difficult time making a self-acceptance statement, as they insist that they don't accept themselves. Some people even cry as they start to make that statement, which is both sad and informing. While this can give you information as to deeper issues to address, it's not a good idea to insist that the client make such a statement of self-acceptance. In these instances, useful variations may include the following:

Even though I [*state the problem*]…

- I'm open to a miracle.

- I choose to feel better.

- I'm safe and secure.

Another option is to simply tap on the little-finger side of the hand without saying anything, since this has often been found to be just as effective.

Tapping Points

There are at least 19 tapping points used in tapping therapies, each of which is associated with an energy meridian. Here are the common tapping points, along with the related meridians:

- Top of head (TOH): governing vessel 20

- Back of head (BOH): governing vessel 17

- Forehead (FH): governing vessel 24.5 (third eye point)

- Eyebrow (EB): bladder 2

- Side of eye (SE): gallbladder 1

- Under eye (UE): stomach 1

- Under nose (UN): governing vessel 27

- Under bottom lip (UL): central vessel 24

- Under collarbone (UCB): kidney 27

- Under arm (UA): spleen 21

- Under breast (UB): liver 14

- Center of chest (CH): central vessel 20 (thymus gland)

- Little fingernail (LF): heart 9

- Middle fingernail (MF): pericardium 9*

- Index fingernail (IF): large intestine 1

- Thumbnail (TH): lung 11*

- Side of hand (SH): small intestine 3

- Back of hand (BH): triple-warmer-3 (gamut spot)

- Inside wrist (IW): meeting points of meridians on the fingers

- Sore spot (SS): a neurolymphatic reflex point on the left side of the chest above the breast; it is rubbed in a circular motion rather than tapped

There are many more acupoints other than those listed here. If you are interested in learning more, I suggest that you review a book on acupuncture. But the points listed here will be enough for you to start tapping.

* These two points do not feature extensively in this book, but they are included here for your reference.

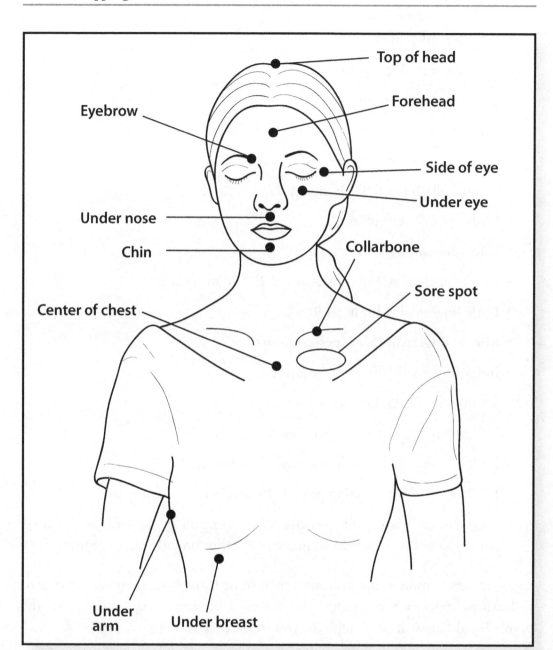

Top of head

Forehead

Eyebrow

Side of eye

Under eye

Under nose

Chin

Collarbone

Sore spot

Center of chest

Under arm

Under breast

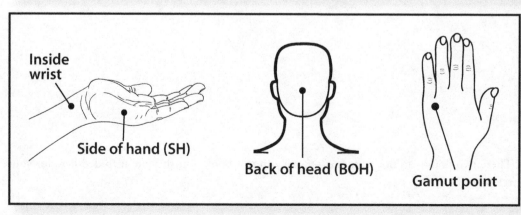

Inside wrist

Side of hand (SH)

Back of head (BOH)

Gamut point

Additional Treatments

There are several additional treatments that are used in combination with tapping. You have already learned one—correction for reversal. Following are directions for several other commonly used treatments. (Even more treatments will be discussed in chapter 5, in the context of troubleshooting.)

9 Gamut Treatments

While it is not always necessary, a useful technique to further reduce the SUD level is the **9 Gamut Treatments (9G)**, which was originally developed by Callahan. This can be used alone or in combination with tapping. When used with tapping, after the tapping points have been completed, you tap between the little-finger and ring-finger carpals on the back of the hand, which is called the *gamut spot* (the third point on the triple-warmer meridian), while doing the following:

- Close your eyes

- Open your eyes

- Look down and to the left

- Look down and to the right

- Move your eyes in a full circle

- Move your eyes in a full circle in the opposite direction

- Hum aloud a few notes of a tune

- Count to five aloud

- Hum aloud again

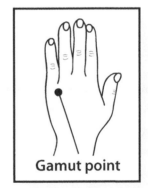

Gamut point

It is assumed that the 9G activates different areas of the brain and the energy system to further tune into the issue and possibly reduce the distress level. After completing the 9G, the tapping sequence is again repeated, using emotional freedom techniques (EFT) tapping points, a thought field therapy (TFT) algorithm, the midline technique (MLT) points, or any other effective sequence. These are covered in the next chapter.

Floor-to-Ceiling Eye Roll (ER)

Another stress reduction technique is the floor-to-ceiling eye roll, or simply the eye roll (ER). To do this, you look down toward the floor without moving your head and then slowly raise your eyes up toward the ceiling while tapping on the gamut spot. The ER can be used as a general stress reduction technique. It can also be used to polish off the treatment after the SUD level is down to 0–2. One or two rounds of ER usually does the trick.

Elaborated Eye Roll (EER)

A useful variation on the eye roll is the elaborated eye roll (EER). This simply involves tapping on the gamut spot and taking a deep breath once your eyes are pointed at the ceiling, extending your gaze up into your forehead, then closing your eyes as you exhale and relax. At this point, you stop tapping and recheck the SUD level. Again, one or two rounds of EER usually lowers the SUD level or stabilizes the results. The difference with the EER is that it increases relaxation, and likely alpha or theta brain waves, by combining higher elevation of the eyes in conjunction with a deep breath.

Words to Tap By

In typical tapping treatment, you help the client tune into an issue, measure their SUD level, and use a tapping sequence. Then you recheck the SUD level and proceed with additional techniques as needed. Some practitioners like to use words to help the client remain focused on the issue at hand. In EFT, these are called *reminder phrases*. After using a setup phrase or reversal correction, words related to the issue at hand are repeated at each tapping point. For example, if someone has a fear of bugs, they might repeat the phrase "squeamish of bugs" while tapping on each of the specified tapping points. They can also repeat variations of this phrase, such as "really bothered by bugs," "can't stand those bugs," "queasy about bugs," and so on. However, it's not always necessary to use words while tapping.

4-8 Breathing

At the end of a tapping sequence, I often like to add the 4-8 breathing exercise. This involves taking a deep breath in through your nose for a count of 4 and breathing out through your mouth for a count of 8. If you can't alternate in this manner between your nose and mouth, simply following this breathing ratio will still help.

Other options include breathing in for 4 and breathing out for 10 or more. The exhale is an important feature of the technique, since it shifts the autonomic nervous system from a state of sympathetic arousal (activation of the fight-or-flight response) to one of parasympathetic relaxation. Give it a try to see how far you can exhale.

The 4-8 breathing technique has been found to improve heart rate variability, which reduces stress, anxiety, inflammation, and pain (Song & Lehrer, 2003). Therefore, I find that this is a helpful addition to any tapping routine. And it's a useful stand-alone breathing technique for general stress reduction.

4-7-8 Breathing

The 4-7-8 breathing technique is based on the pranayama yogic technique. This involves placing your tongue at the roof of your mouth, breathing in through your nose for a count of 4, holding your breath for a count of 7, and exhaling though your mouth for a count of 8. I suggest that you don't cork or tighten your throat (your glottis) while holding your breath to further reduce stress. Simply let the air rest lightly in your lungs. You can also play with extending the length of the exhale on this variation.

Shifting Focus

Another useful addition after completing a tapping routine and 4-8 breathing is to look around and then focus on something in the environment. In this respect, you're shifting your focus externally and away from the internal experience, which is where the stress was activated. I find that this interruption helps to seal in any improvement that you've achieved so far. Next, you return to thinking about the issue. I propose that the original "problem" has been altered, since it was briefly stored into memory—when you retrieve the memory, it is the altered memory that is retrieved and not the original. This may be consistent with the process of memory reconsolidation (Ecker, 2015).

Challenging Results

If the SUD level is down to 0 after you've completed tapping and any extra treatments, it's time to really test the results and push the envelope. The purpose of this is to make sure that you're good to go. A simple way to do this is to see if you can get the distress back. If you're working with a client, you might say, "See if you can really bring back the stress as you think about that issue again." Sometimes it can be useful to have the client talk about the issue out loud, since talking adds another dimension that can make it possible to resurrect the distress. If the client can get back some level of distress, you know that you're not done and that more treatment is needed. Therefore, you continue with the process. But if they can't get back the distress, it's a good sign that you can move on to the next phase, which involves adding a positive outcome.

It's important to tune into the negative—and to neutralize it before attempting to install a positive outcome—because you otherwise have a dispute going on between the negative and the positive. It takes a lot of work to get to the positive when the negative is cooking away, so it's best to tap out the negative before tapping in the positive.

Outcome Projection Procedure (OPP)

Once you've successfully challenged the results—and had the SUD level remain at a 0—you can add a positive outcome with something I call the *outcome projection procedure* (OPP). In neurolinguistic programming (NLP), it's called *future pacing*, but the difference here is that tapping is included.

For example, let's say that you're afraid of dogs. Even thinking about dogs causes a feeling of distress, let alone encountering a dog in real life. However, maybe you tapped it out. You thought about dogs and you felt afraid. Your SUD rating was through the roof. Then you tapped on that fear, and lo and behold, the fear is gone. You feel better now, but what about later? What if you actually see a dog? What if a dog sits right next to you, with its mouth open and drool hanging down? How about petting a dog? Or taking a dog for a walk? This is where OPP comes into play. And there are many ways to do this.

One of the simplest ways is to estimate how much you believe that you will feel fine when you encounter a dog. We could call this your *subjective units of belief* (SUB), with 0 indicating that you don't believe at all that you'll be okay, and 10 indicating that you are absolutely convinced you'll be okay. In this case, perhaps you rate your SUB as a 3. That's a pretty low confidence rating, so it's a good idea to reach a higher SUB to increase your chances of being calm and secure around dogs. All you have to do at this point is to imagine feeling comfortable around a dog and repeat the tapping routine, checking in from time to time on how you feel about being in the presence of a dog. In my experience, when the SUB is 8 or more, you're in good shape.

Certain tapping techniques, like EFT, also involve using preferred reminder phrases while engaging in the tapping routine. For example, while tapping the little-finger side of your hand during the setup, you might say, "Even though I don't have a high level of belief about being safe and comfortable around dogs, I accept myself." Then you would move on to tapping various other locations while repeating the reminder phrase "safe and comfortable around dogs."

Another way to elevate the SUB is to simply tap the gamut spot on the back of either hand while imagining yourself with a dog. At first, you picture yourself "over there" with the dog while tapping. This is a *dis-associated* position—you are viewing yourself from the outside. Continue to check your SUB level until it is within the 8 to 10 range. Next, you *associate* to the image by imagining "being there" with the dog while tapping the gamut spot. Now you see the dog from the perspective of being in your own body. Perhaps you see your hands or other parts of your body, but you don't see your whole self. If distress occurs while doing OPP, it is necessary to go back to the neutralizing phase of treatment and then return to OPP after the distress has been relieved. The purpose of OPP is to install the positive belief, not to neutralize distress.

Debriefing

At the end of a tapping session, it's a good idea to debrief the client. Basically, you go over what happened and also equip the client with the tapping routine that was used. Perhaps you give them a handout that outlines the steps of the procedure so they can repeat it on their own between sessions if necessary. However, I have found that most clients need the assistance of a therapist or coach at first and are not able to do this very well on their own, even with an outline. Practice makes perfect, so you should advise the client not to be discouraged if they don't achieve adequate results on their own, since there is more to the method than meets the eye. Explain that teamwork is an important component, at least at the beginning of acquiring the tapping skill. This is where troubleshooting, understanding, and skills come into play.

When the Work Is Not Complete

You may not achieve complete results in just one tapping session. In such instances, it is helpful to let the client know that it is sometimes necessary to repeat the technique several times. You might even introduce this at the beginning of treatment as a preframe and as a way to relieve performance pressure. You can also do this while doing the tapping technique itself. Ask the client to tap the little-finger side of the hand while saying a reversal correction statement, such as, "Even though we have some more work to do on this issue, we'll continue next time, and I accept myself." However, in most instances, it is sufficient to simply discuss with the client that the treatment is not complete and that you'll continue along these lines at the next session.

The Bigger Picture

Now that you have a variety of tapping techniques and related treatments in your therapeutic toolbox, it's time to put it all together. The next chapter will cover three tapping models that are effective in treating a wide range of issues: thought field therapy (TFT), emotional freedom techniques (EFT), and the midline technique (MLT).

Chapter 4

Putting It All Together

Knowledge comes by taking things apart: analysis.
But wisdom comes by putting things together.

—John Alexander Morrison

Thought Field Therapy

The granddaddy of the tapping therapies is thought field therapy (TFT), developed by Roger Callahan (Callahan, 1985). TFT is a comprehensive approach that offers a variety of treatments, including recipes or algorithms for a wide range of conditions, such as phobias, PTSD, panic attacks, depression, obsessive-compulsive disorder (OCD), and physical pain. TFT also includes diagnostic approaches to individualize the treatment. Here are the steps involved in a comprehensive TFT recipe.

Protocol: TFT

1. Think about the problem, get in touch with the feeling involved, and rate your SUD level.

2. Treat for psychological reversal. Tap on the little-finger side of the hand (SH) or rub the sore spot (SS) while saying three times, "Even though I [*state the problem*], I accept myself."

3. Next, tap on each of the following treatment points five to seven times:

   - Eyebrow (EB)

   - Under eye (UE)

- Under arm (UA)

- Under collarbone (UCB)

- Little fingernail (LF)

- Index fingernail (IF)

- Under collarbone (UCB)

4. If your SUD rating decreases by at least two points, do the 9G treatments by tapping repeatedly at the back of the hand (BH) while doing the following: close your eyes, open your eyes, look down and to the left, look down and to the right, rotate your eyes clockwise, rotate your eyes counterclockwise, hum a tune, count to five, and then hum again.

5. Check the SUD rating, and repeat the sequence starting at step 3. You should repeat the sequence even if the SUD rating is not lower after the 9G, and then check the SUD rating again.

6. If at any point the SUD lowering stalls, repeat the correction for psychological reversal indicated at step 2 with the following variation: "Even though I *still have some* [*state the problem*], I accept myself." Chapter 5 provides other psychological reversals to consider.

7. Continue altering between the series of tapping points and the 9G treatments until the SUD rating is within the 0–2 range. Note that other aspects of the problem may emerge during treatment and should be treated accordingly.

8. Do floor-to-ceiling eye roll (ER) or elaborated eye roll (EER) until the SUD rating is a 1 or 0 (preferably a 0).

9. Challenge the results by trying to get the distress level back. If the SUD rating does not increase, you're done for now. If it does increase and you get back some level of distress, continue with the treatment.

10. Debriefing: If you are working with a client, make sure to teach the client how to treat themselves as needed.

Emotional Freedom Techniques

Emotional freedom techniques (EFT) is a comprehensive tapping sequence or algorithm developed in the 1990s by Gary Craig, who studied with Roger Callahan. In studying the various algorithms and diagnostic approaches, Craig found that he could generally get results by using a one-size-fits-all treatment. However, it should be noted that EFT includes many other elements in addition to tapping and also excludes many aspects of Callahan's method, including the 9G and ER.

Also, in EFT, the psychological reversal distinction is not made. Essentially, it is merely considered to be another aspect of the problem. Nonetheless, the initial phase of treatment (i.e., tapping on the little-finger side of the hand or rubbing the sore spot), combined with the acceptance statement, is still used. In EFT, this is referred to as the *setup statement,* and it maintains two parts that are integral to the approach that Callahan developed: acknowledgment of the specific problem and self-acceptance in spite of the problem. The basic protocol is as follows.

Protocol: EFT

1. Think about the problem, get in touch with the feeling involved, and rate your SUD level.

2. Tap on the little-finger side of the hand (SH) or rub the sore spot (SS) while repeating the setup statement three times. For example, "Even though I [*state the problem*], I accept myself."

3. Next, tap each of the following treatment points five to seven times while using a reminder phrase, such as "this problem":

   - Eyebrow (EB)

   - Side of eye (SE)

   - Under eye (UE)

   - Under nose (UN)

   - Under bottom lip (UL)

- Under collarbone (UCB)

- Under arm (UA)

- Inside wrist (IW)

- Top of head (TOH)

4. Continue with this sequence of tapping points, each time checking the SUD level and any related issues that may come up after a tapping sequence. For example, there may be different scenes involved in a trauma, or different thoughts and emotions involved with some other problem being treated, each being a different aspect to tap on. At such times, the setup and reminder phrases may be altered accordingly.

5. Challenge the results by trying to get the distress level back. If the SUD rating does not increase, you're done for now. If it does increase and you get back some level of distress, continue with the treatment.

6. Debriefing: If you are working with a client, make sure to teach the client how to treat themselves as needed.

Midline Technique

After studying and working closely with Roger Callahan in the 1990s, I developed a diagnostic approach that involves more treatment points and other elements, as well as MLT, which is a one-size-fits-all tapping sequence that contains distinct points and other elements. The basic MLT protocol is as follows.

Protocol: MLT

1. Think about the problem, get in touch with the feeling involved, and rate your SUD level. You can also observe any physical sensations associated with the problem and describe these sensations in their various forms, such as their location, shape, and color.

2. Treat for psychological reversal. Tap on the little-finger side of the hand (SH) or rub the sore spot (SS) while saying three times, "Even though I [*state the problem*], I accept myself, and I choose to be free." You can also choose alternative statements directed toward a positive solution, like "and I choose to be resolved" or "and I'm open to a miracle."

3. Next, tap on each of the following treatment points five to seven times, optionally making a statement about the specific issue at each point:

   • Back of head (BOH)

   • Top of head (TOH)

   • Forehead (FH)

   • Under nose (UN)

   • Under bottom lip (UL)

   • Center of chest (CH)

4. At this point, do 4-8 breathing or 4-7-8 breathing while continuing to tap on the center of the chest.

5. Next, look around and focus on any external object, and then think about the problem again.

6. If your SUD rating decreases by at least two points, repeat the sequence starting at step 3, or do the 9G treatments by tapping repeatedly at the back of the hand (BH) while doing the following: close your eyes, open your eyes, look down and to the left, look down and to the right, rotate your eyes clockwise, rotate your eyes counterclockwise, hum a tune, count to five, and then hum again.

7. Check the SUD rating, and repeat the sequence starting at step 3. You should repeat the sequence even if the SUD rating is not lower after the 9G, and then check the SUD rating again.

8. If at any point the SUD lowering stalls, repeat the psychological reversal correction indicated at step 2 with the following variation: "Even though I *still have some* [*state the problem*], I accept myself, and I choose to be free."

9. Continue altering between the series of tapping points and the 9G treatments until the SUD rating is down to 1 or 0. As other aspects of

the problem arise, treat them accordingly by taking them through the process.

10. If tapping these points doesn't reduce the SUD level to a 0 or 1, do floor-to-ceiling eye roll (ER) or elaborated eye roll (EER) to reduce the SUD level further. You can also use ER or EER even after the SUD level decreases to 0 for good measure.

11. Challenge the results by trying to get the distress level back. If the SUD rating does not increase, you're done for now. If it does increase and you can get back some level of distress, continue with the treatment.

12. Apply the outcome projection procedure (OPP) by imagining your desired outcome while tapping the MLT points or the back of the hand (BH). (See chapter 3 for details.)

13. Debriefing: If you are working with a client, make sure to teach the client to treat themselves as needed.

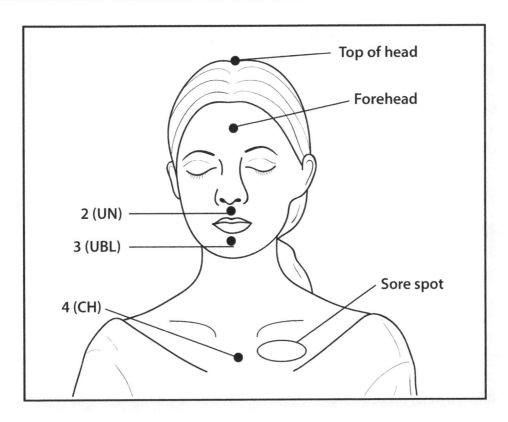

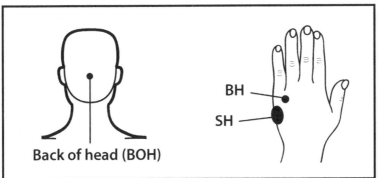

A Composite Narrative

To illustrate how tapping works, following is a vignette of a client named Joe, who represents a composite of various sessions with different people. Although this vignette illustrates the components of MLT, the TFT and EFT protocols could have been applied if MLT had not been moving things along. Sometimes varying the process is helpful.

Joe is 27 years old and lives alone. His parents live nearby, and he is an only child. His parents divorced when he was 12, after which he lived with his father and had visitation with his mother. Both parents are remarried. Joe noted that his mother has a history of treatment for anxiety, but there is no other family psychiatric history to the best of his knowledge. He has also never been in psychiatric treatment or counseling before. He has a high school education and works at a local hardware store.

As with all clients, I begin the session by having a discussion about Joe's concerns, followed by tapping as needed.

Therapist: Good to meet you, Joe. Did you have trouble finding the place?

Joe: Good to meet you too, Doc. No, it was easy to find the office.

Therapist: Good, I know some people get confused with so many offices in this complex. I read over the intake information that you completed, and I see that you've never consulted a therapist before.

Joe: That's right. This is really new to me, and I must admit that I'm a bit nervous.

Therapist: I can understand that, and I'll do my best to make sure that this is a comfortable and maybe even enjoyable experience. Would that be okay with you? [*In a kidding tone and expression.*]

Joe: Absolutely! I was afraid that I would have to let it all hang out and get really stressed. I'd prefer not to do that if it's okay with you. [*Kidding in return.*]

Therapist:	Certainly. Generally, I believe it's better to feel comfortable during treatment rather than getting all worked up and stressed. It's also important that we work together as partners. First thing I'd like to know is what you would like help with. As I said, I read the intake information, but I'd like to hear from you.
Joe:	Well... I get really nervous in social situations. I've always been that way, but it seems like it's getting worse over the past few months. I avoid situations because I'm afraid of facing people. I'm afraid of having a panic attack, which I have had. But mostly I just feel really nervous. So I avoid socializing. I guess I'd like to get over that if it's possible or at least do better.
Therapist:	Okay, so you really get nervous around people, so you avoid them. Is that right?
Joe:	Well, I have a couple of buddies, but that's about it.
Therapist:	What do you think causes the nervousness? What do you think makes you so nervous?
Joe:	I'm not really sure—that's why I came to see you. I even tried medication that my doctor gave me, but one of the drugs made me groggy and the other made me even more nervous. I don't want to be a zombie, and I don't want to be even more nervous than I am. I figured there must be a better way, and a friend recommended that I see you. She said that you have some ways that help people feel better.
Therapist:	Well, I certainly hope that I can help. And I'm sure we can work together on this so you don't have to avoid people so much. But again, I was wondering if you have any thoughts as to what could be causing the nervousness and anxiety. I know you said that you don't know, but I wonder if you could maybe take a guess?
Joe:	Well, like I said, I think I've always been this way. But it's gotten even worse lately. I think it got worse after my girlfriend, Carol, dropped me. It seems like I'm always afraid

that somebody's going to reject me, and I'm waiting for that to happen. I know that sounds silly, but that's what goes through my mind.

Therapist: I can understand that you feel that way. So you've always been nervous, and after the breakup, your nervousness intensified. Is that right?

Joe: Yeah, that's about it. I guess it has something to do with my worrying.

Therapist: That's how it works: We can scare ourselves with our thoughts and memories. That's because there seems to be a one-to-one relationship between our thoughts and our emotions. And sometimes it's really difficult to drop the thoughts and memories.

Joe: Yeah, I try to ignore those thoughts and memories, but that doesn't seem to work. It seems the more I try to push them out of my mind, the more they spring back.

Therapist: That's interesting. It does work that way too. Often, the more we try to get rid of something, the more it sticks around. If you could just accept it, it might go on its way, but that's sometimes difficult—not impossible, but difficult. Sometimes we need a little extra help with letting go. Let's try a little experiment to see if it can help you to let go of those thoughts, those memories.

Joe: An experiment? Like what?

Therapist: Well, there are some techniques that I find helpful in reducing nervousness and resolving painful memories. It may seem odd, but it involves tapping with your fingers at different locations on your body while paying attention to how you feel while recalling a memory or thinking about something you want to do. The places you tap are different locations on your hand, head, and chest.

Joe: I think I heard about something like that on the internet. Seemed kind of weird!

Therapist:	It really does seem weird, but in my experience it works. And there's a lot of research showing that it works too. But the only way to know is to try. It either works or doesn't do anything. If it works, wonderful! If not, no loss. But it's worth a try.
Joe:	Sure, let's try.
Therapist:	What I'd like you to do first is to notice how you feel right now. Do you still feel nervous?
Joe:	Maybe a little bit, but not bad.
Therapist:	Let's see if you can be even more relaxed. I'd like you to notice how you feel in your body and to give your nervousness a rating from 0 to 10, with 10 being the most nervous and 1 being not nervous at all.
Joe:	I'd give it a 4 or 5 right now.
Therapist:	And what word would you use to describe what you feel?
Joe:	I'd say nervous.
Therapist:	Okay, nervous. Now tap on the little-finger side of your hand [*demonstrating*] while saying three times, "Even though I'm nervous, I accept myself, and I choose to feel relaxed."
Joe:	Even though I'm nervous, I accept myself, and I choose to feel relaxed. [*Repeats this statement three times while tapping on the side of his hand.*]
Therapist:	Now I'd like you tap on these points as I tap on myself.

At this point, I proceed to tap on the MLT points on myself—back of head, top of head, forehead, under nose, under bottom lip, and center of chest—while Joe also taps on himself. At times, I guide him to add the reminder phrase of "nervous" or "feeling nervous" while tapping at each of the points. While tapping at the center of the chest, I take him through 4-8 breathing and then ask him to look around the room and focus specifically on something.

Therapist: Now keep tapping on your chest, and breathe in through your nose for a count of 4, and exhale through your mouth for a count of 8. Let's do that again… Now look around the room… and focus in on something like that picture or lamp… Then check again how you feel, Joe, on a scale from 0 to 10.

Joe: I feel a lot better. It's less than a 2.

Therapist: Great! Now, let's do this.

I then guide him through the 9G treatments by having him tap on the gamut spot, between the little-finger and ring-finger carpals on the back of his hand, while doing the following: close his eyes, open his eyes, look down and to the left, look down and to the right, rotate his eyes clockwise, rotate his eyes counterclockwise, hum a tune, count to five, and hum again.

Therapist: What about now, Joe?

Joe: I really feel good. I'd give it less than a 1, maybe a 0.

Therapist: Perfect! Okay just for good measure, I'd like you to do another technique called the floor-to-ceiling eye roll. Tap on the back of your hand right here [*demonstrating*] while very slowly moving your eyes from the floor to the ceiling, then take a deep breath, exhale, relax your eyes, and stop tapping.

Joe: [*Does the eye roll as demonstrated.*]

Therapist: Joe, see if you can get back any nervousness. Give it a try.

Joe: I don't think I want to do that. I feel good right now.

Therapist: I can understand that. But if you would just give it a try, just to see. If you can get it back, all we have to do is tap again.

Joe: [*Makes an effort for about 10 seconds.*] Nope, I can't feel nervous right now.

Therapist: Great! Now how about if we try using tapping to deal with Carol dropping you? Would you like to do that?

Joe: It's hard to imagine that I could feel good about that.

Therapist: I'm sure that really hurt. It's not about feeling good about it; it's about not feeling upset anymore. But bring to mind the specific moment when Carol dropped you, and notice how you feel.

Joe: [*Becomes pensive for a moment while recalling what happened.*] It felt really bad. I feel upset as I think about it now. I'll give it a 9.

Therapist: Okay, Joe, tap on the little-finger side of your hand while saying three times, "Even though Carol dropped me and I feel upset, I accept myself, and I choose to feel better."

Joe: [*Repeats the statements as directed.*]

Therapist: Now let's tap on the same points we tapped on before.

I again proceed to tap on my MLT points—back of head, top of head, forehead, under nose, under bottom lip, and center of chest—while Joe also taps on his. At times, I ask him to add the reminder phrase of "Carol dropped me and I feel upset." While tapping at the center of the chest, I again take him through 4-8 breathing and then ask him to look around the room and focus specifically on something.

Therapist: What would you give it now, Joe?

Joe: Not much of a change if any. I'd say it's still a 9.

Therapist: That's fair. Let's just do another round. [*Repeats the MLT tapping.*]

Joe: That's amazing. [*Laughs.*] It doesn't feel as bad.

Therapist: So what would you give it now, 0 to 10?

Joe: I think a 6!

Therapist: Great! Let's take it further.

I guide him through the 9G treatments again and then have him re-tap the MLT points, followed by 4-8 breathing while he taps the center of his chest. Again, I ask him to look around and then focus on something.

Therapist: How about now?

Joe: Hm! I feel better—no longer upset. I'd give that a 1 or 0. But now I feel some hurt.

Therapist: That's not unusual. Very often there's another emotion underneath. What rating would you give the hurt?

Joe: I'd say a 7.

Therapist: Okay, focusing on the hurt feeling, tap again on the little-finger side of your hand [*demonstrating*] while saying three times, "Even though I feel hurt, I accept myself, and I choose to feel better."

Joe repeats the statements as instructed and then repeats MLT, followed by 4-8 breathing while tapping on the center of the chest, and then looking around and focusing on an object.

Therapist: How about now?

Joe: That's better. A 5!

Therapist: [*Guides Joe through the 9G treatments again.*] How's that now?

Joe: Perfect! I don't feel hurt at all. Actually, I feel pretty good. I'm at a 1 or 0.

Therapist: For good measure, let's do the floor-to-ceiling eye roll again, but this time a bit different. When you point your eyes way up, take a deep breath and then lower your eyelids while exhaling.

Joe: [*Does the elaborated eye roll.*] Feels good. Really relaxed. When I think about it, I'm not upset. Definitely a 0.

Therapist: Okay, let's see if you can get it back. See if you can feel hurt again.

Joe: [*Makes an effort.*] No can do! [*Laughs.*] This is amazing. I'm really thinking about it very differently now.

Therapist: How much do you believe that you'll continue to feel this way?

Joe: Not sure. Depends on if I see her somewhere.

Therapist: Well, right now, if 10 is you absolutely believe that you'll feel okay if you see her, and 0 is you don't believe it at all, where would you put it? Notice that we're changing the scale around at this point, with 10 representing the highest level of conviction and 0 being no conviction at all, a big fat zero.

Joe: I'd say half and half, a 5 or 6.

Therapist: Okay, let's see if we can elevate your confidence level. Having more confidence increases the chances that you'll be good.

Joe: Okay.

Therapist: So, while tapping here [*gesturing to the gamut spot*], imagine running into Carol somewhere, and picture yourself being friendly and confident. I'll ask you from time to time to give me the rating. [*Guiding Joe through OPP*] You can see Carol and Joe over there in the distance and Joe looking and feeling calm, friendly, and confident. Now, just keep tapping on the back of your hand while picturing that. [*After about 20 seconds*] What would you give it now, Joe?

Joe: Feeling stronger, calmer—a 7.

Therapist: Great, keep going... seeing Joe and Carol over there and Joe feeling just fine. [*After about 20 seconds*] And how about now?

Joe: 8... Close to a 9.

Therapist: Wonderful. Keep tapping and seeing Joe feeling calm, confident, and friendly. [*After about 20 seconds*] And now?

Joe: Definitely a 10!

Therapist: Excellent, Joe. Now how about stepping into the image so you're face-to-face with Carol, rather than seeing both of you over there. And keep tapping while you adjust your view. [*After about 20 seconds*] And how's that?

Joe: At first, my confidence came down to a 7, but I'm back up to at least a 9.

Therapist: That's great, Joe. I think we can stop that for now.

Depending on how a person is organized, the outcome projection procedure (OPP) can be a sufficient convincer. Others need some time to pass and need a real-life encounter (or a few encounters) before they are convinced. Regardless, this OPP lays the groundwork.

Joe: I can see why she didn't want to continue with our relationship. I was way too needy at the time.

Therapist: That's quite an insight. What do you make of that?

Joe: I think it goes back to when my parents divorced. I really felt abandoned by my mom when they separated. I stayed with my dad. My mom didn't come around much at first. Things are okay now, but it's funny that still bothers me some.

Therapist: How about if we tap on that?

Over the next several sessions, Joe was also treated for issues related to his parents' separation using MLT, TFT, and EFT. We also focused on his social anxiety and challenged his negative thoughts by tapping, as well as by elevating his awareness of his thoughts and his ability to drop thoughts. Debriefing was also covered at various stages of the treatment, offering him understandings and techniques that he could apply between sessions.

Changing Protocols

When results are not being achieved within a reasonable period of time, sometimes it makes sense to use another protocol. While habituation has certain therapeutic value, it can also result in decreased effectiveness of an approach. The brain seeks novelty, and the benefits of novelty are reduced when you are consistently using the same protocol. Therefore, when EFT is not working, it makes sense to shift to MLT, TFT, or another strategy. And if the tapping doesn't seem to work altogether, rather than give up on this gentle and elegant technique, there are adjustments you can make to get the results you're looking for. The next chapter details additional troubleshooting considerations. Let's call it trouble-tapping.

Chapter 5

Trouble-Tapping

If you always do what you've always done,
you'll always get what you've always got.

—Henry Ford

While tapping generally works to reduce—and even eliminate—stress associated with various conditions, the truth is that nothing works *every* time. Roger Callahan told me that when someone says that their method always works, either they're lying or they haven't treated enough people. Any method will eventually come up against a brick wall, and then it's time to do something else. The following troubleshooting recommendations will help you fine tune and increase the effectiveness of treatment for yourself and others.

Rapport

When the session isn't proceeding well, sometimes it's because rapport has been lost between the therapist and client. Rapport can be lost when the client is distracted, is distressed, or experiences the therapist as being in an overly controlling position. In these instances, checking on and improving rapport will often result in effective treatment. Therapy is best practiced as teamwork, which is why listening is such a highly important aspect of treatment. The deeper you listen, the better the rapport, and the more likely you will realize what the client truly needs.

In addition, if rapport has been lost because a client is feeling distressed or insecure, you need to help the client regain a sense of safety and security. To do so, it is important to calm down the fight-flight-freeze neural circuitry that's been activated. Shifting focus away from the material that is activating the distress is helpful. Additionally, tapping and breathing exercises can calm the nervous system and help the client to feel secure and be more present. You might guide the client to mindfully observe the feelings of insecurity and distress in their body and apply a tapping routine as described in chapter 4. For example:

Therapist: I sense that you're feeling distressed right now?

Client: Yes, I'm feeling really upset.

Therapist: Would you like to talk about it, or would you rather I take you through something that might help reduce your distress?

Client: I'm really too upset to talk about it right now.

Therapist: How about if we do something that helps to calm your nervous system and then we talk about it?

Client: Like what?

Therapist: A simple technique that many people find helpful. It involves breathing and tapping.

Client: Okay, let's try it.

Therapist: Just notice how you feel in your body as you're feeling upset. Notice where you feel this in your body and what it feels like.

Client: In my chest and stomach. It feels tight and rushing.

Therapist: Okay, just notice those sensations of distress without trying to get rid of them. And give those sensations a number on a scale of 0 to 10, with 10 being the most intense.

Client: I'd say a 9.

Therapist: Okay, while you observe those sensations, let's do a specific breathing exercise. Breathe in through your nose for a count of 4, and then breathe out through your mouth for a count of 8. Let me demonstrate first. [*Demonstrates 4-8 breathing.*] Now let's do it together. [*Practices several rounds of 4-8 breathing.*]

Therapist: Okay, how do you feel at this point?

Client: Somewhat better. Not as tight and rushing. I'd say it's a 4.

Therapist: Great! Let's add something else. Tap on the little-finger side of your hand, like this [*demonstrates*], while saying three times: "I accept myself with any remaining tight and rushing feelings, and I choose to feel better."

Client: [*Repeats the reversal statement three times.*]

At this point, the therapist would guide the client through the MLT sequence, followed by 4-8 breathing, looking around the room, and then focusing on an object.

Therapist: How about now?

Client: Much better. I feel really relaxed. I'd say it's less than a 1.

Therapist: Would you like to talk about it now?

Client: Sure. That would be fine.

Finally, rapport can also be lost in relationship to yourself, particularly if you are angry or upset with yourself. The solution is to treat yourself, at least momentarily, with the same level of respect that you would hopefully treat others. Tapping and breathing exercises can also prove beneficial at such times. For example, after tuning into the emotional reactions in your body and observing their various elements (e.g., location, shape, color), you could apply a psychological reversal statement such as "Even though I'm angry and upset with myself, I'm open to feeling better" or "Even though I have this [*specify the various physical sensations*], I choose to feel better." Afterward, apply a tapping routine combined with 4-8 breathing until there is a significant shift in how you are feeling, preferably a reduction in SUD to a 0.

Persistence and Flexibility

Keep on Tapping

While some level of relief is usually experienced after a round of tapping, this isn't always the case. So it's important to keep in mind that, sometimes, many rounds of tapping are needed before some level of relief or total relief will occur. A problem is generally made up of many aspects that require attention before sufficient relief can occur. For example, a trauma may have many moments or scenes, emotions, and beliefs. As you tap, the layers of the onion are peeled away. So keep on tapping. Persistence pays off.

Continuous Tapping

Continuous tapping involves both the therapist and client tapping various treatment points while discussing the client's concerns. This is distinct from specifically tuning into the problem and following a detailed protocol such as EFT in that the client doesn't need to begin with a setup phrase or rate their SUD level. Instead, the client and therapist merely tap continuously while the therapy session proceeds like any counseling session would even without tapping. This makes it possible to step back from the problem and discuss it while reducing distress. It is also often useful for the client to simply tap the points continuously at various times during the day without necessarily consciously bringing anything specific to mind. Often, something negative is cooking under the surface, and the tapping will help to neutralize it even though they are not consciously tuning into it.

Other Forms of Stimulation and Layering

Tapping is one way to stimulate different treatment points, but some people are not comfortable with tapping for various reasons. Some alternatives include the following:

1. Touching (but not tapping) the location points

2. Touching (but not tapping) the location points while taking a breath

3. Imagining tapping or touching the points

4. Watching the therapist or another person tap or touch on themselves

5. Tapping or touching the points on a doll or a picture

6. Running a movie of someone, such as the therapist, tapping or touching the points on themselves

7. Simply verbalizing the tapping points—eyebrow, side of eye, under eye, and so forth (When using setup and reminder phrases, as in EFT, the statements are made after saying the tapping point. For example, "Side of hand—Even though I have this problem…"; "Eyebrow—this problem"; "Under eye—this problem"; and so forth.)

In some instances, it's helpful to combine a number of these variations, what I call *layering*, to improve results. For example, after going through a tapping sequence and tracking their SUD levels, a client might do another round of treatment by touching and breathing, imagining tapping, or simply watching the therapist tap on themselves.

Stabilization

When the client is in severe distress, sometimes tuning into and tapping on a specific issue just won't work. The client is too discombobulated, and their energy is disrupted. It's best to stabilize first. Stabilization can be achieved with 4-8 breathing or 4-7-8 breathing (discussed in chapter 3), heart breathing, containment, resourcing, and/or tapping without words.

Heart Breathing

Heart breathing simply involves placing your hands over your heart and focusing on your breathing, while letting go of thoughts. You allow thoughts to pass through your mind, and whenever you find yourself getting caught up in a thought, you simply return to your breath and the sensations of your hands over your heart. This exercise is a type of mindfulness meditation that also improves heart rate variability and reduces stress. It can be conducted prior to tapping, and it's a useful assignment for clients to practice between sessions because it increases the ability to drop distressing thoughts.

Containment

Containment is another stabilization strategy in which you simply imagine placing the specific issue in a container, perhaps a storage bin or a barrel, and don't attend to the issue while tapping. For example, when treating a client with a history of trauma, you might ask the client to tune into the various scenes involved in the trauma, to rate the distress associated with each scene on the 0–10 SUD scale, and to then place each scene in the container. You then proceed to guide them through a tapping routine such as MLT.

From time to time, you ask the client to guess about the rating or ratings of the items in the container: "Don't really think about the *item itself* that's in the container, but if you were to think about its *rating*, what would you guess the number would be?" You continue along these lines until the client feels pretty certain that the issue wouldn't bother them, after which you ask them to open the container to discover how they feel. If there is some level of distress, they put the items back in the container and tap some more. If there is no longer distress, you challenge the results to make sure they are stable.

Resourcing

Obviously, tuning into a distressing issue can be distressing. It can be very difficult to see the light at the end of the tunnel or to access anything positive. In these instances, a discussion about the client's resources can be quite helpful. Resources can be in the areas of creativity, spirituality, religion, intelligence, family, friends, hobbies, abilities, personality characteristics, positive things they have done in their lives, and so on. As you discuss and locate resources for the individual, it is often useful to have them tap to tune more deeply into the resource. For example, the person may tune into their belief in God and tap the MLT, EFT, or TFT points. Another strategy is to think about the resource while tapping on the third eye point on the forehead, between and slightly above the eyebrows. Whichever strategy you choose, the tapping continues until the client gets in touch with a positive feeling of the resource.

Don't Use Words

While reminder phrases are used in EFT (and invariably in TFT and MLT), sometimes the words can get in the way and create more stress while tapping. I have frequently found that simply tapping without words is highly effective after the client has tuned into the issue being treated. This is the way Roger Callahan originally did the treatment—he simply had the person think about the problem without saying anything about it while tapping as directed.

There are also times when a client may find it difficult to say an affirmation while correcting for psychological reversals. When this occurs, a useful alternative is to simply recognize the problem and to then tap without saying the affirmation. For example, the client can bring the problem to mind and then simply tap on the little-finger side of the hand or rub the sore spot for about 10 seconds. After that, you use a tapping routine, and the SUD level will decrease if the reversal has been disengaged.

Switching

In applied kinesiology, switching or neural disorganization is thought to involve left brain–right brain disorganization. Some of the signs of switching include reversing letters and numbers, confusing your right and left, saying the opposite of what you mean, and acting significantly awkwardly or clumsily. Another way to think of switching is as scrambled energy. The causes of switching can be in one or more of these three areas: (1) a structural imbalance, such as flat feet, a cranial fault, or a spinal subluxation (a misaligned vertebrae); (2) sensitivity to a substance that you have been exposed to or consumed, such as corn, tobacco, or mildew; or (3) severe emotional stress.

When switching occurs, the psychological issue being treated is generally slow to respond or recalcitrant to treatment, so we want to be able to correct it. While getting to the essential cause of switching is important for long-term benefit, even momentarily correcting this condition will help any effective treatment work. One of the simplest brief corrections for switching is to tap on both sides of the bridge of the nose. Sometimes after several seconds of this tapping, the switching is momentarily corrected, making it possible for tapping or other treatments to work efficiently. A more sustaining correction is known as *the hookup*.

The Hookup

1. Place your left ankle over your right ankle.

2. Place your hands out in front of you, arms extended, with the backs of your hands touching.

3. Cross your right hand over and on top of your left hand so your palms are touching.

4. Interlock your fingers and pull your hands and arms in to rest them on your chest.

5. Breathe slowly while resting your tongue against the palate behind your top front teeth.

6. Do this exercise for one to two minutes.

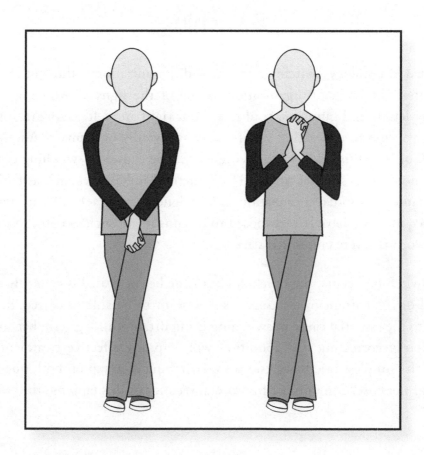

Another correction for switching is the *three polarities correction*, which is also called the *brief energy correction* (Bilazarian, 2018). This is based on the idea that switching involves one or more of three polarities of the body: top/bottom, left/right, and front/back.

Three Polarities Correction

1. Place one hand over the navel while either touching or tapping vigorously under both collarbones, close to the sternum, for 10 seconds.

2. Next, touch or rub under the nose and bottom lip for 10 seconds while holding your other hand over your navel.

3. Finally, touch or rub the coccyx (tailbone) for 10 seconds while holding your other hand over your navel.

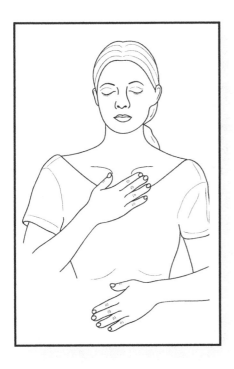
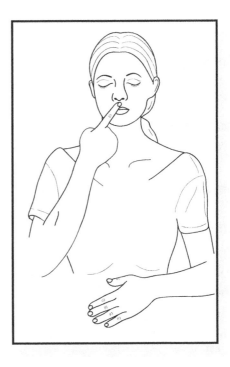

I have found that the hookup and the three polarities correction are also helpful in improving people's focus, such as those with attention-deficit/hyperactivity disorder (ADHD). I take the client through the procedures in the office to see if it helps and then offer the corrections as regular homework assignments. There are also several other corrections for switching, the details of which can be found in *Energy Psychology* (Gallo, 2005) and *Energy Diagnostic and Treatment Methods* (Gallo, 2000).

Psychological Reversals

As discussed earlier, psychological reversal is a condition whereby your motivation is in the opposite direction of your stated intention. Instead of moving in the direction of health or happiness, you move in the direction of ill health or unhappiness. When you are reversed, any potentially effective treatment will not work.

The setup statement used in EFT, which is the same as that used in TFT, addresses **specific reversal**. While tapping on the little-finger side of the hand or rubbing the sore spot, a statement such as the following is used: "Even though I [*state the problem*], I accept myself." However, there are other levels or degrees of psychological reversal. Several of these are outlined next, along with statements and alternate tapping points to correct the reversal. Still others are discussed in detail in *Energy Psychology* (Gallo, 2005).

Mini reversal, also called *intervening reversal*, occurs after some progress has already taken place. For example, let's say that the stress related to a specific problem is measured as a 10. After tapping, the SUD level decreases to a 5. However, progress stalls and remains at a 5 after continuing to tap. This may indicate a mini reversal. To correct for this, tap on the little-finger side of the hand or rub the sore spot while stating, "Even though I still have some [*state the problem*], I accept myself." Note that you can have mini reversals for the other reversals described in this section too.

Recurrent reversal involves the return of the reversal after treatment has proceeded. This is more pervasive than a mini reversal, since the SUD level returns to the same or similar intensity that it was prior to the treatment. For example, if the SUD level was a 10 at the start of treatment, and then decreased to a 5, and then intensified back to a 10, this may be indicative of recurrent reversal. To correct for this, rub the sore spot while saying three times, "Even though I [*state the problem*], I accept myself" or "Even though this [*state the problem*] has returned, I accept myself." It's important to note that an increase in SUD level can also be due to another aspect of the problem that's been activated, and not a recurrent reversal. For instance, if tapping results in a decrease in anxiety, the increase in SUD may be the result of another emotion that has emerged, such as anger, shame, or sadness. In these instances, the treatment continues by addressing the new aspect.

Massive reversal is a pervasive reversal across many contexts or situations, such that it affects many areas of your life. For example, addictive disorders and recurrent depression generally involve massive reversal. At the most basic level, this reversal is treated by using the statement "I accept myself with all my problems and limitations." While making this statement, you tap on the little-finger side of the hand or rub the sore spot on the left side of the chest.

Deep-level reversal involves the unconscious body belief that you are not able to get over the problem and that it will continue indefinitely. The statement used to correct for this reversal is "Even if I never get over [*state the problem*], I accept myself." While the little-finger side of the hand can be used for this correction, tapping under the nose is particularly effective. A statement for the mini version of this reversal is "Even if I never completely get over [*state the problem*], I accept myself."

Safety reversal is the feeling that, at some level, it is unsafe to get over the problem. A correction statement for this type of reversal is "Even if it isn't safe to get over [*state the problem*], I accept myself." While the little-finger side of the hand can be used for this correction, tapping under the collarbone is often effective. For the mini version of this reversal, the statement would be "Even if it isn't safe to completely get over [*state the problem*], I accept myself."

Deserving reversal involves the belief that you deserve to have the problem, which makes it difficult or impossible to resolve the issue until this is addressed. While the little-finger side of the hand can be used for this correction, tapping under the bottom lip is also effective. The accompanying statement is "Even if I don't deserve to get over [*state the problem*], I accept myself." The mini version of the statement would be "Even if I don't deserve to completely get over [*state the problem*], I accept myself."

Deprivation reversal involves the sense that you'll be deprived if you get over the problem. This is especially relevant in cases of addictive behaviors. To correct for this reversal, tap on the little-finger side of the hand or under an eye while stating: "Even if I'll be (or feel) deprived if I get over [*state the problem*], I accept myself." The mini version of the statement would be "Even if I'll be (or feel) deprived if I get completely get over [*state the problem*], I accept myself."

Identity reversal occurs when a person's identity is intertwined with the problem, meaning they identify with the issue as being a part of who they are, which makes it difficult or impossible to effectively treat the problem. To correct for this reversal, you would make the following correction statement while tapping the little-finger side of the hand or the center of the chest: "Even if I lose my identity by getting over [*state the problem*], I accept myself." The mini version is "Even if I lose my identity by getting completely over [*state the problem*], I accept myself."

Finally, **loyalty reversal** is present if, at some level, there is a sense of loyalty in maintaining the problem, such as loyalty to a family member. This reversal is treated by repeating the following statement while tapping at the little-finger side of the hand or the center of the chest: "Even if there is a loyalty issue involved in [*state the problem*], I accept myself, and I chose to be loyal in other ways." The mini version is "Even if there is a loyalty issue involved in getting completely over [*state the problem*], I accept myself."

Other Blocks

Besides reversals, there are a number of other blocks that interfere with treatment. Following are some of the most common blocks and the steps you can take to address them.

Underlying Trauma

If there is a trauma related to the presenting problem, this can get in the way of effective treatment. In these cases, it is necessary to track back to the trauma and apply treatment in that area. For example, if the client is depressed and there is a trauma at the source of the depression, simply tapping on the depression may not result in sustained improvement, but addressing the trauma will. In addition, a current trauma may not resolve if there is an earlier trauma that feeds into it. In these cases, it's best to tap on the earlier trauma first.

Safe Problem

There are also instances where the surface problem is not the real problem. It's the old appearance versus reality conundrum. One example of this is the safe problem, where the problem being presented protects you from having to deal with the real issue. You can get to the core of the real issue by asking, "If this problem were in some way beneficial, what might that benefit be?" or "If this problem were protecting you from something else, what might that be?" For example, someone who struggles with losing weight might really be afraid of having an intimate relationship. Tapping to lose weight could never work, whereas addressing the relationship fears just might result in those excess pounds melting away.

Core Beliefs

When you are focusing on a specific issue, such as social anxiety, you may attempt to tune into and tap on the various reactions associated with this anxiety, such as muscle tension, sweating, or stumbling over words. Although this may prove helpful, generally it's not sufficient because there is usually a core belief underlying these various reactions. This underlying core belief may be along the lines of "I'm not good enough and people don't like me," "People think I'm stupid," or "I'm offensive to others." In these cases, attuning to and tapping on the core belief is essential to experience ongoing relief and transformation. These beliefs may also be rooted in traumatic events that need to be addressed as well.

In EFT, core beliefs are targeted through a process known as *tabletops and legs*, in which the tabletop represents the larger core belief and the legs represent the specific events that give rise to this belief. Essentially, you develop a list of specific events that led to and support the core belief, and then you dismantle the entire structure with the tapping protocol. This pulls the legs out from under the belief so it topples down and is no longer supported.

The tabletops and legs protocol is based on the understanding that core beliefs are broad generalizations of specific events that led to the development of the belief in the first place. For example, someone who believes "I'm not good enough" (the tabletop or broad generalization) may have had specific experiences (the legs) of failing at school, being rejected by someone they were dating in high school, and so forth. The treatment process involves targeting each of the legs and using EFT or other tapping techniques to discharge the emotion of each of the events. As the client experiences relief from each of the events, the core belief dissipates.

This process does not need to be limited to addressing core beliefs, since a patient may have a number of experiences as well as beliefs that factor into their depression. Targeting each of these legs can help to relieve the depression.

Other Troubleshooting Tips

Refocus

Clients who don't attend well and tend to jump around from topic to topic within the same session need some help with focusing. Drawing their attention to this issue and redirecting them can be helpful, as can the heart breathing exercise and a switching correction like the hookup or the three polarities correction. Additionally, you can treat their lack of focus as a type of reversal by having the client tap on the little-finger side of their hand while saying three times, "Even though I am not focusing, I accept myself, and I choose to focus better."

It is also worth considering that clients who come up with different issues at each session may be experiencing a high level of dependency, in which case the dependency issue should be targeted. Again, it can be helpful to explicitly discuss this issue so the client may come to realize their dependency, and this may also be treated as a reversal and benefit from tapping.

Take a Break

Focusing on an issue in therapy can be tiring and stressful. Therefore, taking a break can be beneficial. You might stand up and walk around, do some stretching, or talk about something pleasant for a while. Then when you return to the topic at hand, tapping or other techniques may work better. Taking that break can give you renewed energy, inspiration, and focus.

Drink Water

If you are experiencing some level of dehydration, tapping therapies may not work efficiently (or at all). A simple solution is to have a few sips of water. This is often helpful, although the exact reason for it is up for grabs. The energetic explanation is that it improves the flow of energy. However, it may be that drinking water is a useful interrupter and is soothing in itself.

Check on the Therapeutic Contract

When you're not getting results by tapping, an important thing to consider is the therapeutic contract. The contract is what you and the client have agreed to work on. It's always possible that you and the client have very different objectives in mind, so it's important to check on this. It should also be clear that the therapeutic contract may have a shelf life and can change. Best to keep your eye on the ball.

Ask the Client What They Think

When you're not getting anywhere with tapping or any other technique, it's often useful to ask the client what they think. Basically, you drop it in the client's lap: "We've been really working on this issue, and we don't seem to be getting anywhere. What do you make of this?" This can shed new light on the issue and what's needed. For example, you may find out that the client hasn't really committed to tapping or any other techniques you've taken them through because they just wanted to talk things out. They wanted you to listen, to ask them some fair questions, and to point them in a direction. Your commitment should always be on what the client needs in order to achieve a positive result. Never be committed to the technique as much as to benefiting the person and their desired outcome.

One additional consideration is the client's level of motivation. Does the client really want to change? Not everyone who comes to therapy or coaching is there to change. They may want to feel better, but they don't necessarily want the change to come from themselves. They may want someone else to change, or they may want a situation to change that may be beyond their control. It's a good idea to find where the client is along the spectrum. Then you can decide if it makes sense to continue in this way or to call it a day.

Apex Problem

After clients experience an improvement or a resolution in their problem, there are some who won't believe that the tapping had anything to do with this effect. Certain clients will even claim that they overstated the intensity of the problem or that it never existed in the first place. Others will insist that they were distracted or that the improvement was due to something else, such as the therapist's use of affirmations or the placebo effect. Callahan called this the *apex problem*, borrowing the term from British writer Arthur Koestler (Callahan, 2001). In these cases, the client is acting as a "left-brain interpreter," in which they basically interpret new findings with already accepted explanations (Gazzaniga & LeDoux, 1978). Most of us who use tapping techniques have encountered the apex problem, which I see as a form of cognitive dissonance. But what to do about it?

If these issues aren't handled, it's likely that the client will discount the technique and refrain from using it or not be receptive to using it in sessions. This is unfortunate, since tapping techniques can be highly effective. To address this problem, my tendency is to acknowledge the client's position and to have a discussion about the effectiveness of the approach. I often point out that I, too, felt the technique was absurd when I first heard about it, so I can appreciate how they feel. I might even tell the client that we're kindred spirits. I point out that even though I felt better after using the techniques, I just couldn't believe that the tapping had anything to do with it. I saw it as a trick, a distraction, a placebo—as something superficial.

I also admit that it took a long time for me to realize and accept the value of the technique but that I eventually couldn't ignore the facts. If the client comes around to giving it a chance, we go forward. If they are really strongly opposed, I point out that tapping isn't the only way to get results, and most importantly, I want to help them feel better and get the results they're seeking. I'll return to the possibility of tapping at a later time if we're not getting results in other ways. However, as effective as a technique might be, we always place the client and their health first and foremost in mind and heart—over the technique.

There are many other ways of handling the apex problem, such as sharing with the client your prediction that they might discount the treatment even though they'll feel better. Putting the objections up front can take the wind out of the sails and reduce the credibility of any future objections. Sometimes I also have the client write their SUD level on a piece of paper before the tapping begins, in case they conclude that they were not particularly distressed before we began treatment. Afterward, the record may help them recognize the significant change that occurred and allow them to be open to continuing treatment with this approach.

One final comment: I find that, sometimes, clients are resistant to using an effective approach if the presenting problem is a safe problem or there are secondary or primary gains involved. In such instances, the apparent resistance is important information that can help you to help the client. This might be a time for a heart-to-heart discussion. And if given a chance, we might even tap on that.

Getting Specific

Once a client is open to using tapping, the results can truly be life-changing. The next few chapters explain how to use tapping to treat chronic issues that are limiting your clients' lives: trauma, PTSD, pain, depression, anxiety, and phobias. Specific techniques and case examples illustrate how tapping can alleviate these painful issues.

Chapter 6

Transforming Trauma and PTSD

Trauma is a fact of life. It does not, however, have to be a life sentence.
Not only can trauma be healed, but with appropriate
guidance and support, it can be transformative.

—Peter A. Levine

Amanda's Trauma

Amanda was a 19-year-old college student who had PTSD as a result of a severe automobile accident involving a head-on collision with another vehicle. The other driver—who was intoxicated at the time—was killed, as were his passengers. Amanda was pinned under her dashboard for over three hours while a rescue team freed her from the car. She was life-flighted to a hospital, after which she spent several months in a rehabilitation center and in a wheelchair. When I saw her 11 months after the accident, she had been experiencing frequent nightmares, flashbacks, panic episodes, generalized anxiety, and feelings of guilt and anger related to the traumatic event.

Amanda and her mother participated in the initial session, at which time an intake and a detailed history were obtained. I also focused on developing rapport with her, given that this is an important aspect of promoting stabilization and security. Toward the end of this first session, I told Amanda that I had some techniques that often help people resolve trauma quickly and painlessly. I said that I didn't know if this would help her at the moment, since we only had about 10 minutes left in the session, but I wanted her to get a sense of the kind of work we would be doing in future sessions.

She agreed to continue, and I asked her to think about an aspect of the trauma—specifically a scene of the accident—that still bothered her. She focused on being pinned under the dashboard, and recalling this caused her to experience a SUD level of 9. Rather than asking Amanda to hold the memory in mind, I asked her to imagine putting it in a container, perhaps a box or storage bin, for safekeeping. I then asked her to imitate me as I tapped my fingers at the various points involved in the MLT protocol: back of head, top of head, forehead, under nose, under bottom lip, and center of chest. As we went through the MLT protocol, I intermittently reassessed her SUD level.

After one round of MLT, I asked Amanda not to bring the trauma to mind but to simply guess what the level of distress would be if she were to recall it vividly. "Still a 9," she said. I told her that was fine and that we should repeat the tapping procedure. Then I guided her through another round of MLT tapping points, after which I asked her to estimate her level of distress again. This time she said, "I feel more relaxed. I think it might be a 6."

Next, I took her through the 9G treatments. After this, she estimated that her SUD level would be a 3 if she were to really think about the event vividly. After two more rounds of MLT followed by the floor-to-ceiling eye roll (ER), Amanda said that she didn't think it would bother her if she were to "really" think about being pinned under the dashboard. So I asked her to check it out. After reviewing the scene for a couple of seconds, she laughed and enthusiastically responded, "Wow! It doesn't bother me now! How does that work?" I told her that while I would be happy to explain this to her, I wasn't sure she had given this a fair test yet, so I asked her to review the memory in more detail to be sure that it did not bother her. After about 10 seconds, she shook her head, laughed, and reported that it still didn't bother her.

Next, I asked Amanda to do one more test. I set a timer for one minute and asked her to try to become distressed about the memory while her mother and I talked over a few things. I explained that if she could feel distress about any aspect of the event, that would mean that we needed to do some more treatment on that memory. I asked her to picture the event in vivid detail—the way her body was positioned in the car, the front seat cramping her in, the sounds of the rescue workers cutting her out of the car, and so on. Amanda tried her hardest to become upset about this vivid memory, but she was unsuccessful. She laughed with enthusiasm again. "It's amazing! No big deal now! How does that work?" I pointed out that I wasn't absolutely sure if it had worked thoroughly and that we would know better at the next session, at which time we could do more treatment on the event if necessary.

To my delight, our follow-up sessions one week, two weeks, and two months later revealed that after this initial treatment, Amanda no longer experienced trauma symptoms surrounding this aspect of the car accident. During the course of therapy, various other aspects of the trauma, including survivor guilt and anger, were treated similarly using either MLT or other treatment protocols. We only needed 10 sessions from start to finish.

How can results such as these ultimately be explained? While psychological problems can be viewed cognitively, neurologically, chemically, and behaviorally, they are fundamentally energetic. Our bodies and nervous systems operate electrically and electromagnetically at both profound and subtle levels. This is even the basis of medical technologies such as electroencephalography (EEG), electrocardiography (EKG), and magnetic resonance imaging (MRI). Fundamentally, everything in our material world is energy, even our thoughts and emotions.

Therefore, when a traumatic experience occurs, it results in a strong emotional electromagnetic charge that is captured by the nervous system and the body as a whole, similar to the way that information is stored on a computer hard drive or MP3. To entertain a mixed metaphor, imagine tossing pebbles into a pond and leaving an ongoing record of the ripples as the pond freezes instantly upon impact. There's the information record. Then by attuning to the trauma (the ripples) and activating subtle energy systems (turning up the heat), the stored information is released. The memory imprint is dissipated, or entropy is introduced, to borrow a term from physics. Then a new memory of the event is formed that no longer holds the distressing emotional charge. Ripples gone, smooth waters! Energy-based methods such as TFT, EFT, and MLT thaw the pond and offer a new lease on life.

You can also view the efficacy of EP from the lens of the autonomic nervous system. When a traumatic event occurs, our amygdala sends a signal to activate the sympathetic nervous system, which prepares us to fight or flee from the event. In this state of sympathetic activation, we cannot adequately process information through our memory centers, specifically the hippocampus. Therefore, once the traumatic event is over, we are unable to recognize it as a distant memory; instead, it becomes stuck and is experienced as an ongoing present danger. Tapping works to calm the amygdala, after which people generally report feeling calm and that the memory of the event has become vague and distant.

In addition to the sympathetic nervous system, our autonomic nervous system also consists of a parasympathetic branch, which can be further separated into a dorsal vagal complex and a ventral vagal complex (Dana, 2018; Porges, 2011). The dorsal vagal complex is an evolutionary older branch of the parasympathetic nervous system that becomes activated when the traumatic event involves a life threat from which there is no escape, causing us to collapse or shut down. In contrast, the ventral vagal complex, also known as the social engagement system, is activated under conditions of safety, and it facilitates connection and relaxation.

With PTSD, the dorsal vagal branch remains activated even after the event is over, causing the nervous system to shut down, numb out, and disconnect from others even when no danger is present. Tapping works to normalize this sympathetic-parasympathetic ebb and flow, neutralizing the effects of trauma and shifting you back into a state of social engagement so you can feel safe and secure, relate to others, and experience love, joy, and playfulness.

Next, I'll discuss various types of trauma that tapping has proven effective in treating, as well as some specific protocols for these traumas.

Types of Traumas

Type I Trauma

Trauma can be categorized in terms of level of severity and the individual's resilience and developmental history. Single incident trauma, also referred to as type I trauma (Terr, 1994), is most common following a single traumatic event in which major emotional distress is experienced and the person has the ability to return to a normal daily routine fairly quickly. However, some people continue to experience emotional distress for an extended period of time, causing significant disruptions to their day-to-day functioning that can result in a diagnosis of PTSD. They experience symptoms like nightmares, flashbacks, intrusive memories or dreams, and an exaggerated startle response. They are also prone to intense distress when exposed to internal or external cues that remind them of the event, causing them to avoid these situations and thoughts altogether.

Type IIA Trauma

Type II trauma involves multiple events, rather than a single incident (Terr, 1994). With type IIA trauma, the person is able to separate or compartmentalize the traumatic events. One trauma doesn't bleed into another, and each can be treated as a single traumatic incident. Generally, these people have fairly stable backgrounds that have provided them with the resources needed to separate traumatic events.

Treating Type I and Type IIA Trauma

Type I and type IIA traumas generally respond well to trauma-focused approaches, such as tapping, EMDR, cognitive therapies, and visual-kinesthetic disassociation (VKD). For tapping, you can use the protocol that follows. Since a traumatic event usually involves several scenes, this protocol involves treating each scene individually. Alternatively, treating the most significant scene or aspect of the event may result in a decrease in or elimination of distress related to the other scenes.

Protocol: Type I and Type IIA Trauma

1. Bring to mind the traumatic event, get in touch with the feeling involved, and rate your SUD level.

2. Treat for psychological reversal by tapping repeatedly on the little-finger side of hand (SH) or rubbing the sore spot (SS) while saying three times, "Even though I have this trauma, I accept myself, and I choose to feel relief." You can also consider other reversals covered in chapter 5.

3. If using the containment technique, place the trauma scene or scenes in an imaginary container and don't focus on them throughout the process. With this technique, you intermittently guess about the SUD level until you think there will be no distress, at which time you think about the event or scene to confirm that this is the case.

4. Next, tap on each of the following treatment points five to seven times (or, alternatively, tap on the EFT or MLT points):

   • Eyebrow (EB)

   • Under eye (UE)

   • Under nose (UN)

   • Under bottom lip (UBL)

   • Under arm (UA)

   • Under collarbone (UCB)

   • Little fingernail (LF)

   • Index fingernail (IF)

5. Check your SUD rating. If there is no decrease, go back to step 2 and cycle through the sequence again. If there is no decrease after several rounds, there is possibly another reversal or switching that needs to be addressed (see chapter 5).

6. When the SUD rating is down by at least two points, do the 9G treatments by tapping repeatedly at the back of the hand (BH) while doing the following: close your eyes, open your eyes, look down and to the left, look down and to the right, rotate your eyes clockwise, rotate your eyes counterclockwise, hum a tune, count to five, and hum again.

7. Check the SUD rating again, and continue alternating between the series of tapping points and the 9G treatments until the SUD rating is within the 0–2 range. Sometimes the treatment needs to be repeated several times before there is complete or near-complete relief.

8. When the SUD rating is 0 to 2, do the floor-to-ceiling eye roll (ER) until the SUD rating is a 1 or 0 (preferably a 0).

9. Challenge the results by trying to see if you can get the distress level back. If the SUD level does increase, repeat aspects of the treatment— perhaps only the ER or the tapping sequence.

10. When the distress is finally gone, apply the outcome projection procedure (OPP) by imagining your desired outcome while tapping on the back of the hand (BH).

11. Debriefing: If you are working with a client, make sure to teach the client how to treat themselves as needed, but also advise them to have a moratorium on thinking about the trauma until the next session.

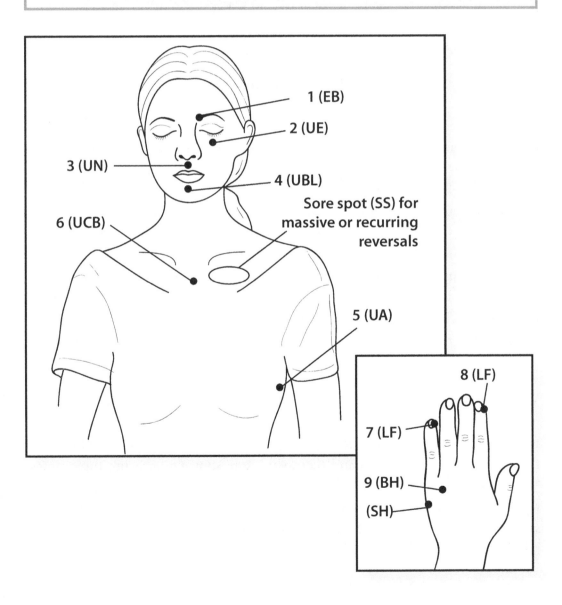

Chronic Trauma

In contrast to type I and type IIA traumas, there is chronic trauma, which involves ongoing traumatic experiences that occur during the developmental years (and even later). This can include events such as child abuse, sexual assault, domestic violence, bullying, and combat experiences. Oftentimes, survivors of chronic trauma exhibit intense confusion, have difficulty managing their emotions, and tend to overreact to misperception in their environment. They also have body memories (bodily and emotional sensations related to the trauma that are triggered without associated cognitive awareness), impaired memories (inability to recall details of the event), and avoidance of thoughts or situations that remind them of the event. Acting-out behaviors like sexual promiscuity, fighting, and substance abuse are also common.

Type IIB Trauma

Type IIB is type of chronic trauma in which a person experiences multiple traumatic events and is unable to separate them, causing them to bleed into one another (Terr, 1994). While this type of trauma may be treated with trauma-focused tapping techniques like TFT and EFT, considerable preparation is generally needed. The relationship with the therapist is paramount, and there must be an emphasis on creating a secure environment, both within the therapy session and in the person's life outside of therapy. Techniques to prevent dissociation and high levels of distress during treatment are needed. Breathing exercises, the hookup, and containment (discussed in chapter 5) are helpful in this respect. These are practiced in sessions and as assignments between sessions. It's also important to attune to the traumatic memory scenes only briefly and not delve into them, since that can be retraumatizing.

When clients are unable to separate multiple traumas and treat them as single incidents, you can address this issue by correcting for specific, deep-level, and massive reversals. For example, to correct for specific reversal, you would tap on the little-finger side of the hand or rub the sore spot while saying three times, "Even though I'm overwhelmed with traumas, I accept myself, and I choose to feel safe and secure." For deep-level reversal, you would tap under the nose while saying three times, "Even if I will never be able to separate the traumas, I accept myself, and I'm open to a miracle." And for massive reversal, you would rub the sore spot while saying three times, "I deeply accept myself with all my problems and limitations."

Type IIB trauma is usually not an area where tapping techniques can be successfully applied without the assistance of a therapist, so correction for psychological reversal would be done many times over the early stage of treatment as the relationship solidifies between the therapist and client. After this, specifically tapping on traumatic events can be conducted. With some clients, though, it is better to use alternative stimulation techniques, such as lightly touching the acupoints with the fingertips, since tapping can trigger neuroception related to their trauma.

Here are some other suggestions for helping clients with chronic trauma to maintain stability, prevent traumatizing abreaction, and instill the ability to compartmentalize:

- Discuss areas in the client's life where they are able to compartmentalize, and heighten their awareness about how they can do that. If the client has no experiences with being able to compartmentalize, help them brainstorm about resources. Practice this in sessions and between sessions.

- Help the client become aware of the feeling that precedes their tendency to jump from one memory to another, and assist them in dissipating those triggers by applying breathing exercises and tapping routines.

- Improve neural organization and the client's ability to focus by applying techniques such as the hookup and brief energy correction.

- Practice heart breathing on a regular basis, which can help to improve focus and emotion regulation, as well as instill a deeper sense of well-being.

- Offer assignments that can improve focus and flexibility, such as walking or running meditation, yoga, preferred sports activities, music, and singing.

Type IIB(R) Trauma

Yet another kind of chronic trauma is type IIB(R) trauma, in which someone with an otherwise stable background experiences overwhelming trauma that strips them of the resources needed to remain resilient (Terr, 1994). In these cases, it is necessary to rebuild the client's resources before attempting to apply trauma-focused techniques. One important resource that you must build is the client's ability to separate and compartmentalize in general, as well as to eventually separate traumas in the way that a type IIA individual is capable.

Sessions can also involve accessing resources that the person has historically had and applying visualization and tapping to solidify those resources. For example, if a client used to enjoy dancing, you can help them reclaim this resource by having them recall memories about this activity and use tapping to access the positive feelings associated with it. I have found that engaging in tapping or other point stimulation while having the client recall these positive memories— as well as having them imagine themselves engaging in the activity—generally intensifies the positive feelings and increases their chances of engaging in the activity. This is essentially the outcome projection procedure (OPP). Here is a useful protocol.

Protocol: Type IIB(R) Trauma

1. Think about your preferred activity, and using a 0–10 scale, rate your level of enjoyment in this activity as you think about it now.

2. Tap on the little-finger side of the hand (SH) while saying three times, "Even though I used to enjoy [*the resource*], I accept myself, and I chose to enjoy [*the resource*] again."

3. Tap on the gamut spot while recalling and imagining the resource until the positive feelings intensify into the 8–10 range.

4. If tapping the gamut spot doesn't elevate enjoyment, tap the MLT or EFT points, followed by prolonged tapping on the gamut spot.

5. If tapping still doesn't help to elevate enjoyment, correct for deep-level reversal by tapping under the nose (UN) or on the little-finger side of the hand (SH) while saying, "Even if I never enjoy [*the resource*], I accept myself, and I chose to enjoy [*the resource*]."

6. Assuming that the resource is reclaimed, you can engage in the identified activity and use tapping as needed to support improvement.

The case of Barbara covered in chapter 3 is an example of type IIB(R) trauma. Although tapping worked well to neutralize the emotional distress she attached to the traumatic memory, this was preceded by a solid therapeutic relationship based on unconditional acceptance.

Type IIB(nR) Trauma

Finally, type IIB(nR) trauma occurs when someone never developed resources for resilience in the first place, since the traumas occurred so early in life (Schore, 1994). Here, resilience and resource building become the primary focus of therapy, and the relationship with the therapist and other significant people in their life is of utmost importance. Similar to type IIB(R) trauma, an important resource to access and develop is the ability to separate and compartmentalize in general and eventually to separate traumas in the way that a type IIA individual is capable. In these cases, trauma-focused techniques can be used only after a significant improvement in functioning has occurred. The same recommendations offered for type II(R) trauma apply here, although the client needs help in developing resources for resilience, as opposed to accessing what they have stored somewhere in their neurology and energy.

Remember, the therapist's health can resonate and impact the client, and it can serve to access the client's inner health and strengths. With type IIB(nR) individuals, building rapport and a strong therapeutic relationship is of utmost importance, as this allows a client who has never developed adequate resources to do so within the context of the therapeutic relationship. The potential is already there in the same way that neuroplasticity is already there. The use of psychological reversal corrections, tapping routines, breathing exercises, and the other interventions described in this book can be truly powerful within this kind of relationship.

Chapter 7

From Pain to Gain

Pain is only bearable if we know it will end, not if we deny it exists.

—Viktor Frankl

Recently, an 85-year-old man named Ben arrived at my office, in pain and walking with two canes. He was there for a spinal cord stimulation (SCS) trial clearance and was accompanied by his son. SCS is a medical procedure that involves inserting a device in the body that sends an electrical impulse up the spinal cord, blocking pain signals from getting to the brain. Ben had previously undergone a spinal fusion but still had severe back pain. During the interview, he said that he didn't want another surgery, as he was upset that the fusion did not relieve his pain and that he could now also feel "the cage that the surgeon put in my spine." I explained that the purpose of the evaluation was to determine whether SCS was appropriate for him and that it was up to him if he wanted to have a stimulator surgically implanted.

I also asked if he would like to try an alternative treatment, which basically involved having him observe the pain while I tapped on the back of his hand at the gamut spot between his little-finger and ring-finger carpals. (Generally, I have the patient stimulate the point themselves in the office, but I varied my approach to make it easier for him to follow the other directions of this approach.) Within about 10 minutes, his pain was gone. He was able to get up from his chair and move about the office without the help of canes. He immediately exclaimed, "Did you hypnotize me, Doc?" I said I didn't think so, and I asked him if he thought he was hypnotized. After a brief moment, he agreed that he hadn't been hypnotized. He also reported that the feeling of the "cage" was gone.

At this point, I explained that people usually can't do this treatment on their own at first because it takes time to get proficient with the technique. However,

I still showed Ben's son how to do the technique for his father, which they practiced in session. A week later, Ben returned to the office to complete the inventories that I recommended for the SCS clearance. He told my assistant, "I'll complete the forms the doc wants, but that tapping works! I haven't even needed pain medication." From then on, he was able to use this technique to manage his pain, and he opted not to proceed with SCS.

Pain and Punishment

Pain is a Middle English term that comes from the Latin word *poena* and the Greek word *poinē*, meaning punishment, penalty, and payment. These roots are true to the experience. Obviously, none of us are strangers to pain. For my part, pain has paid me a visit in ways that have increased my understanding of it. Following my severe automobile accident at age 21, which left my spleen ruptured and my kidneys bruised, I suffered excruciating pain both in the moments leading up to surgery and as I recovered in intensive care. And it was intense pain! When I called out to a nurse about needing something to help with the pain, she told me I would have to wait an hour and a half, since it was too early to get another morphine injection according to the doctor's orders. (In those days, pain medication was given by an intramuscular injection, rather than by a patient-controlled analgesia pump.)

As I lay there in bed, consumed with pain and wondering, "What can I do?" it occurred to me that the pain I was experiencing was at least as intense as the pain I had felt in the emergency room when I first arrived at the hospital. Actually, the pain was probably even stronger, since now I also had a large incision where the surgeon removed my spleen. I was actually frightened about the pain, too, since it seemed that it would not relieve and would even get more intense if I didn't have a shot of morphine.

Then I had an epiphany: I realized that while the pain was more intense now than it was prior to the surgery, it was actually quite different, even acceptable. The pain in the emergency room was what could be called "dying pain," while this was now "surviving and healing pain." That thought gave me a sense of security and even gratitude. And although the pain continued, it was no longer as intense, and this honest reframe gave me a feeling of security. It was now possible for me to be present with the pain from a different emotional and consciousness perspective. I stopped being preoccupied with the pain as something awful. I could relax.

As a result of this and other experiences with pain, I developed an interest in helping others who suffer with pain. In time, my practice as a psychologist has led me to specialize in the treatment of pain and trauma. Besides using hypnosis, visualization, and biofeedback, sometime after 1992, I began to apply EP techniques such as tapping for the relief of pain.

Pain Complexity

On the biological side, pain involves three aspects of the nervous system: the peripheral nerves, spinal cord, and brain. The peripheral nerves extend from the skin, muscles, and internal organs to the spinal cord. Many of these nerves contain nociceptors—cells that sense real or potential damage to the areas of the body where they are located. When injury occurs, these cells send electrical impulses along the peripheral nerve to the dorsal horn of the spinal cord. Then specialized chemicals called neurotransmitters are released and stimulate other spinal cord nerves to transmit information about the injury to the brain. These signals travel to the thalamus, a relay station that sends signals to three distinct regions of the brain: the somatosensory cortex (where physical sensations are registered), the limbic system (where certain emotions occur), and the frontal cortex (where you do much of your thinking, attending, and planning).

But pain is not simply a biological response to an injury or disease; it is also psychological and social. For example, it is well known that emotional reactions, such as depression and anxiety, can also serve to magnify pain, which can in turn intensify the emotional reaction. That's because the circuitry of pain is intertwined with our emotions. In some respects, pain can even be considered an emotion, as both emotions and pain involve physical sensations and share circuitry. Therefore, if the emotional reaction to the pain can be altered, the experience of pain follows suit. Shifting our perception of pain has a way of making it more tolerable, more acceptable, and less intense (as I learned from my experience in intensive care after surgery).

Pain can also elicit sympathy from others who, in turn, may come to the injured person's rescue, which is another survival feature of pain. However, in the case of chronic pain, the sympathy can also reinforce the experience of pain, similar to how giving a reward in response to a particular behavior will increase the frequency of that behavior recurring. And, at times, sympathy can serve as a way to gain more sympathy and even to manipulate others. In this respect, pain is socially systemic in that it's often a family affair.

The experience of pain is therefore a composite of physical sensations, emotions, and thoughts. And successful intervention often needs to address all three, and even more. This is consistent with the gate control theory of pain (Melzack & Wall, 1965, 1982), which maintains that pain signals travel from the body to the dorsal horn of the spinal cord and then to various areas of the brain, and that pain signals can be reduced by certain kinds of bodily stimulation as well as by altering thoughts, attention, and emotional reactions.

While there are injuries that cause chronic pain, pain can also be intensified by habitual tension, postures, and movements that wear away at joints and vertebrae (Warren, 2019). For example, bending your neck to text can result in a habitual posture that places strain on your neck, causing vertebrae damage as well as neck, upper back, and shoulder pain. Becoming conscious of these postures and regularly correcting them can alleviate the root cause of chronic pain and prevent further damage.

What's More: Energy+

Fundamentally, all matter is energy arranged in various patterns, or what Buckminster Fuller called *tensegrity* (Fuller, 1961). Human beings, and possibly all sentient beings, are consciousness, energy, and spirit at their core. We have values and beliefs that also show up in patterns. Attending to these basic aspects of pain sensations is also an important aspect of treatment. Energy psychology proposes that treatment at the energy level incorporates the whole. That is, when we treat pain by observing it and possibly by tapping, we are treating the pain energetically and also chemically, neurologically, cognitively, emotionally, and socially.

The Value of Pain

There is value in pain: It serves as a signal that something is wrong and needs to be attended to, protected, and corrected. The same holds true for our emotions. Each emotion is a signal to pay attention. For example, fear informs us about danger, anger prepares us to fight, shame protects us from being ostracized by the group, sadness primes us to grieve, and so on.

While acute pain can have a beneficial purpose, in many respects, chronic pain does not fulfill this criterion. It's an ongoing, stuck pain that involves a confusing message, as if it's acute pain that requires protecting the area with rest. Sometimes chronic pain can even cause a person to reduce their activity to the point where their muscles atrophy, or to brace against the pain so that its intensity increases. People can hate the pain, be angry about the pain, feel worthless because of the pain, and so on. All of those factors contribute to what is referred to as *chronic pain syndrome*. The following are some practical ways to help people in such situations.

Pain Relief Protocols

Triple-Warmer-3 (TW3) Technique

One way to help relieve pain is to mindfully observe the pain features and the associated emotional sensations while tapping at specific acupoints. By applying this process, the tension and emotions release, and the experience of pain then becomes more acceptable and diminishes greatly, sometimes being eliminated altogether. You can accomplish this with the triple-warmer-3 (TW3) technique, which involves focusing on the pain, observing it in its various aspects, relaxing into those sensations, and letting go of bracing against the pain, and then simultaneously holding, rubbing, or tapping between your little-finger and ring-finger carpals on the back of either hand (gamut spot) while attending to your breathing and continuing to monitor the level of pain. You can also add some extra benefit by practicing 4-8 breathing while tapping.

The intensity of the pain typically begins to diminish within a few minutes, and in many cases, the pain dissipates altogether. As part of this protocol, you may also attend to each of the emotions associated with the pain, one after the other, applying the same technique. As the emotions dissolve, so does the pain.

Protocol: TW3 Technique

1. Focus your attention on the pain, describe its sensations (e.g., location, shape, color), and rate its intensity on the SUD scale from 0 to 10.

2. Treat for possible reversal by repeatedly tapping on the little-finger side of the hand (SH), by tapping the back of the hand (BH), or by rubbing the sore spot (SS) on the left side of the chest while saying three times, "Even though I have this pain, I accept myself, and I choose to feel relief." If necessary, consider other reversals (as discussed in chapter 5).

3. Tap at the back of the hand (BH) extensively, and periodically switch to tapping under your collarbone (UCB), alternating between these points until there is a decrease in pain of two or more SUD points.

4. If there is no decrease in pain, go back to step 2 and repeat the sequence. If there is no decrease after five minutes, this may not be an adequate treatment for your pain, or there is another reversal to correct. Switching, which is covered in chapter 5, may also be involved.

5. Next, do the 9G treatments by tapping repeatedly at the back of the hand (BH) while doing the following: close your eyes, open your eyes, look down and to the left, look down and to the right, rotate your eyes clockwise, rotate your eyes counterclockwise, hum a tune, count to five, and hum again.

6. Again, rate the pain intensity on a scale of 0 to 10. As long as there is a decrease in the level of pain, continue with the technique until there is little or no pain remaining. If the treatment stalls at any point, this suggests a mini reversal. Treat this by tapping at the little-finger side of the hand (SH) while saying three times, "Even though I still have some pain, I accept myself and I choose to feel relief." Sometimes the treatment needs to be repeated several times while focusing on the pain before there is a complete or near-complete relief from the pain.

7. When the pain level is 0 to 2, do the elaborated eye roll (EER) to lower the pain further or to complete the treatment effects. To do this, tap on the back of the hand (BH), hold your head straight, and using only your eyes, look at the floor and then slowly and steadily raise your eyes up toward the ceiling. While looking up at the ceiling, take a deep breath, close your eyes, and slowly exhale. Alternatively, do the floor-to-ceiling eye roll (ER).

8. Debriefing: If you are working with a client, show them how to use the protocol to reduce pain when necessary. It's important to point out that it may take time and lots of practice before they develop proficiency with the technique.

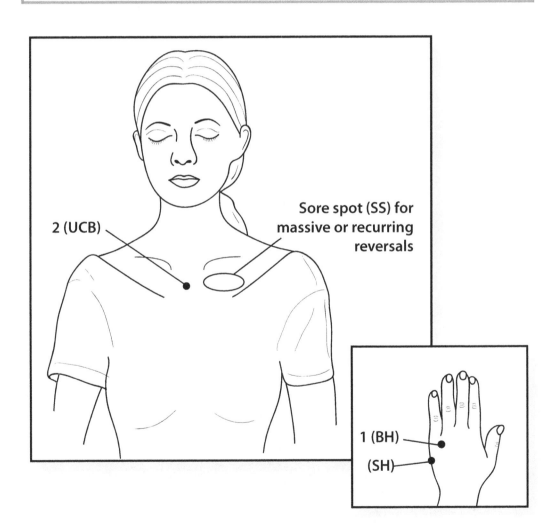

2 (UCB)

Sore spot (SS) for massive or recurring reversals

1 (BH)

(SH)

TW3 Plus Technique

When the basic TW3 technique doesn't help, it's often useful to embellish the technique by adding treatment points. There are several ways to do this, including EFT, MLT, or TW3 plus. The TW3 plus technique is similar to the basic TW3 technique, but additional treatment points from TFT are included.

Protocol: TW3 Plus Technique

1. Focus your attention on the pain, describe its sensations (e.g., location, shape, color), and rate its intensity on the SUD scale from 0 to 10.

2. Treat for possible reversal by repeatedly tapping on the little-finger side of the hand (SH), by tapping on the back of the hand (BH), or by rubbing the sore spot (SS) on the left side of the chest while saying three times, "Even though I have this pain, I accept myself and I choose to feel relief." If necessary, consider other reversals (as discussed in chapter 5).

3. Tap several times at each of these locations:

   - Eyebrow (EB)

   - Under eye (UE)

   - Under nose (UN)

   - Under bottom lip (UBL)

   - Under arm (UA)

   - Under collarbone (UCB)

   - Little fingernail (LF)

   - Index fingernail (IF)

4. If there is no decrease in pain, go back to step 2 and repeat the sequence. If there is no decrease after five minutes, this is probably not an adequate treatment for this pain, or there is another reversal to correct. Switching may also be involved.

5. Next, do the 9G treatments by tapping repeatedly at the back of the hand (BH) while doing the following: close your eyes, open your eyes,

look down and to the left, look down and to the right, rotate your eyes clockwise, rotate your eyes counterclockwise, hum a tune, count to five, and hum again.

6. Again, rate the pain intensity on a scale of 0 to 10. As long as there is a decrease in the level of pain, continue with the sequence until there is little or no pain remaining. If the treatment stalls at any point, this indicates a mini reversal. Treat this by tapping at the little-finger side of the hand (SH) while saying three times, "I accept myself with this remaining pain." Sometimes the treatment needs to be repeated several times while focusing on the pain before there is complete or near-complete relief from the pain.

7. When the pain level is 0 to 2, do the floor-to-ceiling eye roll (ER) to lower the pain further or to complete the treatment effects. To do this, tap on the back of the hand (BH), hold your head straight, and using only your eyes, look at the floor and then slowly raise your eyes up toward the ceiling. Alternatively, do the elaborated eye roll (EER).

8. Debriefing: If you are working with a client, show them how to use the protocol to reduce pain when necessary. It's important to point out that it may take time and lots of practice before they develop proficiency with the technique.

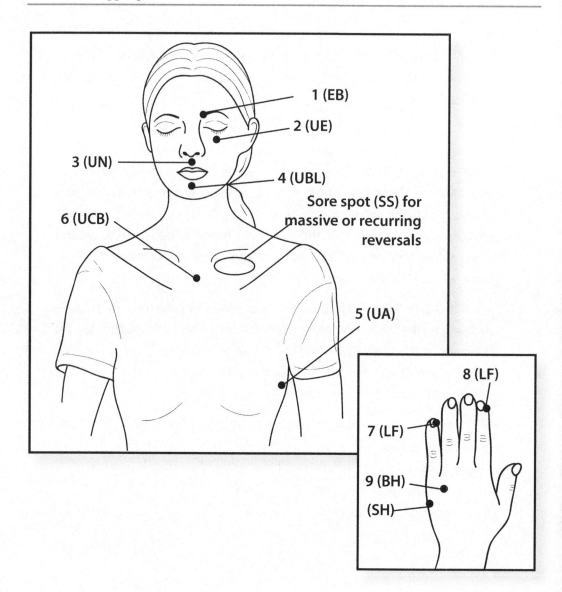

1 (EB)

2 (UE)

3 (UN)

4 (UBL)

Sore spot (SS) for massive or recurring reversals

6 (UCB)

5 (UA)

8 (LF)

7 (LF)

9 (BH)

(SH)

Other Treatment Considerations

When using these protocols to reduce pain sensations, there are several important considerations. If there is a traumatic event involved in the pain condition, treating the trauma using the techniques covered in chapter 6 will be necessary to see accompanying reductions in pain.

Additionally, other emotions, thoughts, and beliefs are often connected to the physical pain. Understandably, the person may hate the pain, feel embarrassed or ashamed about it, or feel hopeless, guilty, angry, or depressed. Given that these emotional reactions can intensify the pain, it makes good sense to reduce these reactions using some reversal statements and associated reminder phrases (in italics). For example:

- "Even though I *hate the pain*, I accept myself and choose to let go of the hate."

- "Even though I feel *embarrassed about the pain*, I accept myself, and I choose to let go of the embarrassment."

- "Even though I feel *hopeless about the pain*, I accept myself, and I am open to a miracle."

- "Even though I *worry about the pain*, I accept myself, and I let go of the worry."

- "Even though I'm *angry about the pain*, I accept myself, and I choose to let go of the anger."

- "Even though I feel that *my life is over because of the pain*, I accept myself, and I choose to have a good life anyway."

There are many other EP, cognitive, and mindfulness techniques for managing and treating chronic pain that have not been covered in this chapter. However, what has been covered here is fairly robust and can prove of considerable help. Additionally, it should be emphasized that these techniques are for the purpose of managing chronic pain that has not adequately responded to other medical treatment. They are not a substitute for medical treatments such as surgery, physical therapy, transcutaneous electrical nerve stimulation (TENS), medication, epidural injections, radiofrequency ablation, spinal cord stimulation, and other medical approaches.

Chapter 8

Up from Depression

Depression is an empty and hopeless feeling
as you set your gaze on the future and see nothing.

—Anonymous

The Depression Formula

It is clear that a number of factors figure into the development of depression. First of all, certain areas of your brain are more intricately involved in the process, such as the amygdala and thalamus, which activate emotional reactions and regulate consciousness and alertness. In addition, the dorsal branch of the vagus nerve operates a freezing and shutting-down process that results in withdrawal from social interactions and feelings of shame. There are also chemical aspects to depression, including disruption of neurotransmitters such as serotonin, dopamine, and norepinephrine. These chemicals serve as conductors of the electrochemical current that operates within your nervous system. Too little and you become sluggish, uninterested, hopeless, and even anxious or worried.

But what triggers depression in the first place? In most cases, these brain and chemical changes don't happen in a vacuum. It would seem that something must set the depression ball in motion, rolling down the hill to the valley below. Frequently, depression is triggered by certain events that have occurred, whether recently or in the distant past. These events are traumatic to some degree and involve real or anticipated loss. This can include the death of a loved one, unemployment, health problems, financial problems, and so forth. The event must involve a loss that is perceived to be of great significance. That's because depression doesn't simply arise from the event itself, but from how we *perceive* and *interpret* it. When someone is depressed, they have negative thoughts about the loss, which triggers their ensuing emotional reaction.

However, depression is not solely a function of external events. External factors may serve as triggers, but depression cannot be reduced to these factors alone. Rather, depression is a complex interplay of elements such as genetic vulnerability, family history, hereditary factors, and brain structure. Depression can also be a function of unconscious thoughts and perceptions. Although there are many interrelated causes of depression, in the EP sphere, the most fundamental cause is believed to be related to thought and energy.

Our thoughts carry certain energy markers that allow for the entire chain of causes involved in depression to take place. Depression involves negatively charged thoughts that carry messages to our senses throughout our bodies. Even thoughts that are generally considered to be positive may contain depression-stimulating energetic features. For instance, thinking about a wonderful, loving relationship that you had in the past can trigger thoughts of loss and depression. Thoughts can both precede and follow the feelings of depression, but they're still an intricate aspect of the depression formula. Therefore, while there are many causes of depression, the thought-energy connection seems to be the most fundamental.

To illustrate the connection between thoughts and emotions, picture a lemon as clearly as you can. Imagine its shape, size, and color. Maybe you get a sense of how it would feel in your hand. Now imagine cutting that lemon in half and biting into it. What happens? If you're like most people, you get a reaction in your mouth—a sour-pucker reaction. Maybe you cringe and tighten your facial muscles, or maybe you smile. The mere thought of the lemon activates these physical sensations. It also activates positive or negative emotional reactions, depending on whether you like or abhor sour foods. But where is the lemon? It's simply a thought in your mind.

More apropos to tapping would be a traumatic memory. When you attune to the memory (which is a type of thought), either consciously or as a result of unconscious neuroception, you experience an emotional reaction. It might be panic, dissociation, shame, depression, or any combination of these. After tapping and neutralizing the emotional reaction, the memory no longer bothers you. The memory is still there, but it's less clear, less relevant, and definitely in the past. You no longer panic, dissociate, or feel ashamed or depressed. While these changes can be explained in neurological terms (involving the hypothalamic-pituitary-adrenal axis and the dorsal vagal complex), in EP, these changes are viewed in terms of energy. In particular, the distressing emotions associated with trauma are thought to be a result of energetic markers that were contained in the memory. That is, the distress does not result from the memory itself. Collapsing these energetic markers, which Callahan called *perturbations*, thus neutralizes the distress that accounts for the trauma.

This same process applies to any emotional state, including depression. When someone is depressed, they can experience discouraging thoughts about their life, hopelessness, nihilism, and suicidal ideation. These thoughts have an impact because of the perturbations, not exclusively because of the thoughts themselves. A person who is not depressed could entertain these same thoughts, but they would be empty, without emotional charge. In addition, individuals with depression tend to engage in behaviors that further reinforce the depressed affect, such as moping, withdrawing, maintaining a slouched posture, and avoiding social interactions.

With these factors in mind, the formula for depression might be as follows:

1. A genetic predisposition exists in your family of origin.

2. A loss or stressful event occurs.

3. You have frequent unsettling thoughts about this event.

4. The thoughts are unsettling because they contain certain disrupted energy markers (perturbations).

5. Certain areas of the brain involved in emotion become further activated by the disrupted energy in the thoughts to produce negative emotions.

6. Neurochemicals go out of balance as they become depleted through the process of the disrupted or perturbed thoughts.

7. Different behaviors and social interactions may occur that further reinforce this chain of events, such as moping, avoiding social contact, exhibiting depressed facial features and movements, and so on.

8. And now we have a good deal of depression.

Tapping Out Depression

Of course, here we are discussing theory, and there is a fairly detailed theory about energy systems and emotions. But the important thing to know is that when you are depressed, your energy system is out of balance, and it can be returned to balance through EP techniques such as tapping. These treatments serve to remove the most basic cause of the depression, which is within the realm of energy. By tapping on specific energy points in specific ways, the negative energetic features in the thoughts are removed, your energy system becomes balanced, and the depression is relieved. Think of depression as being caused by an energy field—much like the magnetic impressions on a computer hard drive that allow you to store and access information. By tapping, you stimulate the energy system, which causes that field to be interrupted and erased, thus erasing the depression.

There is ample research to support the effectiveness of this technique. A meta-analysis of 20 quality scientific studies showed that tapping was effective in reducing depression in a variety of populations and settings, with tapping being equal or superior to treatment-as-usual and other active treatment controls. What's more, these effects remained large whether the treatment was delivered in groups or individually, and these gains were maintained over time (Nelms & Castel, 2016).

Of course, given the thought-energy connection, another important component of treatment is being able to recognize when you are entertaining thoughts that are part and parcel of depression—and to then rise above them and let them go. It's important to note that letting go of depressive thoughts does not mean suppressing them. When you suppress, you're just trying to push the thought out of your mind, but you hold the thought as true and believe that it has power over you. Rather, letting go involves making a shift in your understanding where you recognize that the real cause of depression is the thought-energy connection.

As you allow the depressive thoughts to evaporate, you will come to see that they were not truths at all, but a distorted way of thinking about your life and yourself. These thoughts only seemed true because your emotional energy system was disrupted. In essence, these thoughts were a mirage or an illusion, and you became *disillusioned* by them. This is not to say that undesirable things aren't happening or haven't happened in your life; that may very well be the case. But the depression is another matter, and it is a function of your thoughts causing disruptions to your emotional energy. As you hone your awareness of the connection between thoughts and feelings, in time you may not even have to tap. You eventually develop the ability to shift from a state of distress to one of security and serenity, just by recognizing the state you're in and moving upward to healthy psychological functioning.

Mark's Depression

Mark had been experiencing depression for over six months. He was depressed about a number of things in life—he had recently broken up with a long-term girlfriend and, on top of that, he was dissatisfied with his job and perplexed about where he was going in his career. His physician had placed him on an antidepressant medication, but he did not find that it was helping. He had never had psychotherapy before, so he decided to give it a try. When I first saw Mark, I administered the Beck Depression Inventory (BDI), a 21-item instrument that covers the main symptoms of depression: insomnia, depressed mood, low energy, fatigue, suicidal thoughts, and so on. His results indicated severe depression.

After discussing the various issues involved in his depression, I advised Mark about the possible benefits of tapping. I explained that while antidepressant medication can be helpful, depression is often caused by negative thoughts we have about the events in our lives, and there is an electrical aspect to these thoughts that can be relieved quite rapidly with certain techniques. However, I also emphasized that he needed to practice not getting caught up in depression-producing thoughts. I offered him a way to accomplish this, which involved using reminders (sticky notes placed in various areas of his life space, such as his car and his home) to nip depressing thoughts in the bud and applying a tapping routine (which I will describe in the next section). We discussed the fact that continuing to focus on these negative issues would result in energy and chemical imbalances and would negatively affect his nervous system. Mark took this advice to heart.

Next, I asked him to focus on the feeling of depression and to rate it on a scale of 0 to 10. He gave it an 8 at the time. I also asked him to describe the way his depression felt, and he reported that it felt like a burning in his face, a tightness in his throat, and an empty feeling in his chest and stomach. As Mark observed the location and intensity of these sensations, I had him tap on the back of his hand at the TW3 point (the gamut spot located between the little-finger and ring-finger carpals).

After a couple of minutes, with no appreciable change in his feeling, it seemed possible that there was a psychological reversal blocking the effectiveness of this treatment. I therefore directed him to continue tapping while repeating several times, "I accept myself with these depression sensations in my face, throat, chest, and stomach." Within a matter of seconds, he started to experience some relief. Before long, the feelings had decreased to a 5. I had him tap under his collarbone several times and then return to tapping on the TW3 point. This was combined with some other treatments, and within several minutes, the depression sensations dissipated.

After we finished tapping, I again emphasized the importance of not getting caught up in depressive thinking and reviewed the tapping treatment we'd done so he could repeat it during the week if necessary. When Mark returned for his session the following week, notable improvement was evident on the BDI. He was no longer severely depressed, although mild depression was still evident. We repeated the treatments from the previous week, and the residual depression dissipated in the session. At his next follow-up visit, the BDI indicated no evidence of clinical depression, and Mark was rather amazed at what had transpired in such a short period of time. "It's uncanny!" he exclaimed.

Eventually, I contacted Mark's physician about his progress in treatment, and he tapered and eventually discontinued the antidepressant medication. We had several follow-up visits intermittently over the course of a couple months, and since there was no return of depression, treatment was discontinued with the understanding that Mark could return for additional treatment should the need arise. A follow-up telephone contact six months later revealed that there was no recurrence of depression. Mark was doing quite well.

TW3 Technique

Similar to treating chronic pain, a basic EP treatment for depression is the TW3 technique, which involves tuning into the physical sensations of depression, observing these sensations in their various forms (including their location, shape, and color), and then simultaneously tapping between your little-finger and ring-finger carpals on the back of either hand (the gamut spot) while attending to your breathing and continuing to monitor your SUD level.

Protocol: TW3 Technique

1. Focus your attention on the sensations of depression—describing them in detail—and rate your depression on the SUD scale from 0 to 10.

2. Treat for possible reversal by repeatedly tapping on the little-finger side of the hand (SH) or on the gamut spot on the back of hand (BH) between the little-finger and ring-finger carpals while saying three times, "I deeply accept myself even though I'm depressed" or "I accept myself with these depression sensations: [*specify sensations*]."

3. Tap extensively at the back of the hand (BH), and at times, briefly tap under your collarbone (UCB), while continuing to observe the depression sensations. Consider doing 4-8 breathing.

4. Rate your depression again. If there is a decrease of at least two points, move on to the next step; if not, go back to step 2 and cycle through the sequence again. If there is no decrease after three attempts, this may not be an adequate treatment for your depression, or there is another reversal to correct. (See chapter 5 for details.)

5. Next, do the 9G treatments by tapping repeatedly at the back of the hand (BH) while doing the following: close your eyes, open your eyes, look down and to the left, look down and to the right, rotate your eyes clockwise, rotate your eyes counterclockwise, hum a tune, count to five, and then hum again.

6. Then repeat tapping at the back of the hand (BH) and under the collarbone (UCB). Consider doing 4-8 breathing again.

7. Again, rate your level of depression on a scale of 0 to 10. As long as there is a decrease in the level of depression, continue with the sequence until there is no depression remaining. If the treatment stalls at any point, this indicates a mini reversal. Treat this by tapping on the back of the hand (BH) or the little-finger side of the hand (SH) while saying three times, "I deeply accept myself, even though I still have some of this depression." Sometimes the treatment needs to be repeated several times before you feel complete relief.

8. When the depression level is 0 to 2, do the floor-to-ceiling eye roll (ER) to lower the distress further or to complete the treatment effects. To do this, tap on the back of the hand (BH), hold your head straight, and using only your eyes, look at the floor and then slowly and steadily raise your eyes up toward the ceiling.

9. Challenge the results by trying to get back the feelings of depression. If you can feel depressed, continue with the tapping routine. If you cannot feel depressed, move on to the next step.

10. Apply the outcome projection procedure (OPP) by tapping on the back of the hand (BH) while installing the conviction that you will continue to feel well. Check your level of conviction (with 10 being the strongest) periodically while you tap.

11. If the feelings of depression return at a later time, repeat these treatments. In time, recurrence of depression symptoms should become less frequent.

12. Debriefing: If you are working with a client, show them how to use the protocol between sessions. It's important to point out that it may take time and lots of practice before they develop proficiency with the technique.

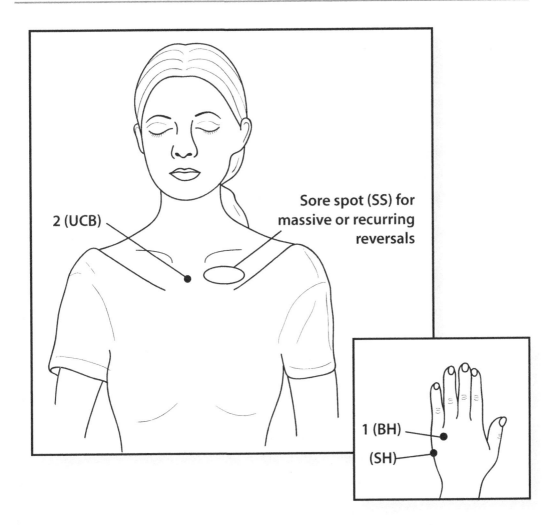

2 (UCB)

Sore spot (SS) for massive or recurring reversals

1 (BH)
(SH)

When TW3 Isn't Enough

When TW3 does not significantly relieve or alleviate the depression, it may be due to switching or another level of psychological reversal that must be corrected before the depression treatment will work. However, in other instances, it is not a matter of a reversal. Rather, it's that your energy system is more pervasively in a state of disruption, which requires more treatment points. In this case, you can combine additional treatment points from the TFT, EFT, or MLT protocols to address the various emotional and cognitive aspects that arise in relation to the depression. These aspects may include different emotions—such as shame, sadness, and worthlessness—as well as the thoughts, painful memories, and beliefs at the source of these emotions.

The following protocol includes the TFT and TW3 points.

Protocol: TFT and TW3

1. Focus your attention on the sensations of depression—describing them in detail—and rate your depression on the SUD scale from 0 to 10.

2. Treat for possible reversal by repeatedly tapping on the little-finger side of either hand (SH), by tapping on the back of the hand (BH) between the little-finger and ring-finger carpals, or by rubbing the sore spot (SS) on the left side of the chest while saying three times, "I deeply accept myself even though I'm depressed" or "I accept myself with these depression sensations: [*specify sensations*]."

3. While lightly focusing on the depression sensations, tap repeatedly at the following points and consider doing 4-8 breathing after tapping the sequence:

   - Eyebrow (EB)

   - Under eye (UE)

   - Under nose (UN)

   - Under bottom lip (UBL)

   - Under arm (UA)

   - Under collarbone (UCB)

   - Little fingernail (LF)

   - Index fingernail (IF)

4. After completing the above sequence, identify the location for the meridian points for the back of the hand (BH) and under the collarbone (UCB). While observing the depression sensations again, tap on the back of the hand (BH) extensively until you notice a decrease in depression, and then tap under the collarbone (UCB) several times. Consider doing 4-8 breathing.

5. Rate your depression again. If there is no decrease, go back to step 2 and cycle through the sequence again. Persistence will usually pay off.

6. Next, do the 9G treatments by tapping repeatedly at the back of the hand (BH) while doing the following: close your eyes, open your eyes,

look down and to the left, look down and to the right, rotate your eyes clockwise, rotate your eyes counterclockwise, hum a tune, count to five, and then hum again.

7. Repeat the tapping points and consider doing 4-8 breathing after tapping the sequence:

   - Eyebrow (EB)

   - Under eye (UE)

   - Under nose (UN)

   - Under bottom lip (UBL)

   - Under arm (UA)

   - Under collarbone (UCB)

   - Little fingernail (LF)

   - Index fingernail (IF)

8. Again, rate your level of depression on a scale of 0 to 10. As long as there is a decrease in the level of depression, continue with the sequence until the depression level is 0 to 2. If the treatment stalls at any point, tap on the little-finger side of the hand (SH) while saying three times, "I deeply accept myself, even though I still have some of this depression." Sometimes the treatment needs to be repeated several times before you feel substantial or complete relief.

9. When the depression level is 0 to 2, do the floor-to-ceiling eye roll (ER) to lower the distress further or to complete the treatment effects. To do this, tap on the back of the hand (BH), hold your head straight, and using only your eyes, look at the floor and then slowly and steadily raise your eyes up toward the ceiling. Alternatively, do the elaborated eye roll (EER).

10. Challenge the results by trying to get back the feelings of depression. If you can feel depressed, continue with the tapping routine. If you cannot feel depressed, move on to the next step.

11. Apply the outcome projection procedure (OPP) by tapping on the back of the hand (BH) while installing the conviction that you will continue to feel well. Check your level of conviction (with 10 being the strongest) periodically while you tap.

12. If the feelings of depression return at a later time, repeat these treatments. In time, recurrence of depression symptoms should become less frequent.

13. Debriefing: If you are working with a client, show them how to use the protocol between sessions. It's important to point out that it may take time and lots of practice before they develop proficiency with the technique.

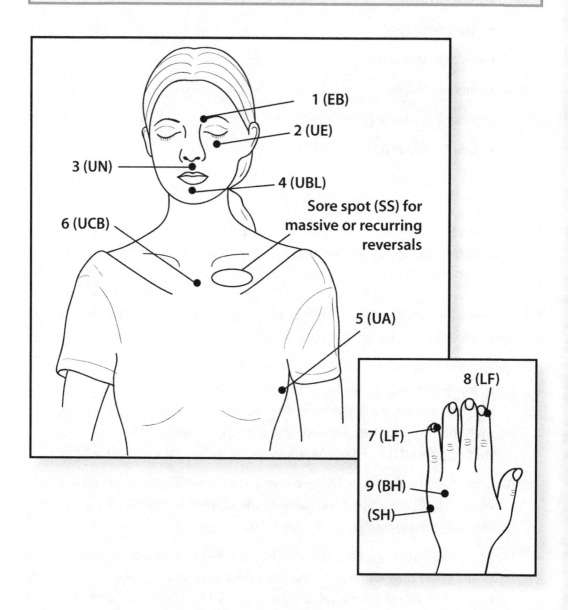

Other Treatment Considerations

There are several important considerations when using tapping to treat depression. If there is a traumatic event involved in the depression, alleviating the trauma will be necessary in order to experience a significant decrease in depression symptoms. Additionally, other emotions, thoughts, and beliefs are generally integral to the depression, including feelings of hopelessness, anger, low self-esteem, anhedonia (reduced ability to experience pleasure), thoughts of death or suicide, lowered sexual desire, fatigue, and irritability. While targeting the generalized sensation of depression may afford significant relief, you may also need to direct treatment at the specific components. Here are some reversal statements and associated reminder phrases (in italics) to treat these components:

- "Even though I *feel depressed*, I accept myself, and I choose to let go of the depression."

- "Even though I *feel hopeless*, I accept myself, and I am open to a miracle."

- "Even though I'm *angry at myself*, I accept myself, and I let go of the anger."

- "Even though I *don't feel enjoyment*, I accept myself, and I choose to feel enjoyment."

- "Even though I *have low self-esteem*, I accept myself, and I choose to feel better."

- "Even though I *have suicidal thoughts*, I accept myself, and I let go of suicidal thoughts." (Important note: Hopelessness and suicidal thoughts are often lethal symptoms that are best treated in a safe and secure environment.)

- "Even though I've *lost sexual desire*, I accept myself, and I am open to a miracle."

- "Even though I *feel fatigue and loss of motivation*, I accept myself, and I choose to let go of the fatigue."

- "Even though I *feel irritable*, I accept myself, and I am open to a miracle."

Although I have provided detailed tapping protocols in this chapter that have proven effective in treating depression, self-help is not always sufficient. If you find that you have been able to use these suggestions to alleviate depression, wonderful! However, if the treatments have not proven sufficient, I strongly advise you to not take this as an indication that effective help is not available. Depression is exceedingly treatable, so I encourage you to contact a qualified mental health professional, specifically one who can help you with regard to the EP approach covered in this book.

Chapter 9

Calming Anxiety and Phobias

There is nothing to fear but fear itself.
—Franklin D. Roosevelt

Although fear and anxiety are similar in many ways, they are also quite different. Fear is a reaction to real and imminent danger. It causes your body's autonomic nervous system to go into high alert, activating the fight-flight-freeze response as a means of preparing you to deal with the danger. In contrast, anxiety is primarily a mental activity involving worry, tension, and vigilance that occurs in relation to some possible future danger. However, the body's reaction to anxiety is similar in that it also activates the stress response, priming you to fight, flee, or freeze.

While there are many types of anxiety disorders, in this chapter I focus on generalized anxiety disorder (GAD), panic disorder, separation anxiety disorder, and several types of phobias. I'll describe the specific characteristics of each condition and provide some general tapping treatment protocols.

Generalized Anxiety Disorder

GAD involves persistent, uncontrollable, and chronic worry about everyday life events. Individuals with this condition often experience symptoms such as restlessness, edginess, fatigue, difficulty concentrating, blanking out, irritability, muscle tension, and sleep problems. Although the average age of onset is 30 years, many people with GAD report that they've been anxious their entire lives. Indeed, the condition is often chronic, although the intensity tends to vary across the lifespan, and rates of complete remission tend to be low without treatment. But with focused treatments like tapping, GAD can be managed and even eliminated.

A detailed review of the research has supported the beneficial effects of EP and tapping in treating anxiety and related conditions, with one study of over 5,000 patients finding a 90 percent positive response and a 76 percent complete elimination of symptoms with EP, compared to a 63 percent positive response and a 51 percent complete elimination of symptoms with CBT and medication (Andrade & Feinstein, 2004).

When using tapping techniques for GAD, you begin by tuning into the sensations of anxiety and applying TFT, EFT, or MLT to calm the nervous system. You can then target any memories or worries that are associated with anxiety. For example, there may have been a traumatic event connected with the GAD, and the person may worry that similar events will occur in the immediate future. There may also be worries that are unrelated to past events but are nonetheless replete with anxious trepidation. To a large extent, it's a function of worry and a "when's-the-next-shoe-going-to-drop" state. By tuning into and tapping on these memories and worries, the emotional aspects of the thought become disengaged and neutralized. This is a bottom-up and top-down process. Anxiety, which is an autonomic visceral state, can trigger associated thoughts and memories (bottom up), and thoughts and memories can trigger anxiety (top down). You need to treat the anxiety from both directions to be thorough.

The following is a modified protocol based on EFT, although other protocols can be effective as well. When treating a client, you don't just jump into tapping without taking preliminaries into account. After establishing rapport, ask pertinent questions about the various aspects involved in the anxiety response. What are their specific worries? When did this all begin? What does the person believe about themselves? This provides fodder for the treatment. As you ask these and other questions and listen, inspirations will occur about the most relevant aspects to tap on. At this point, you may proceed as follows.

Protocol: GAD

1. Focus on the anxiety sensations—describing them in detail and mindfully observing them without judgment—and rate your anxiety on the SUD scale from 0 to 10.

2. Tap on the little-finger side of either hand (SH) or rub the sore spot (SS) on the left side of the chest while saying three times, "I deeply accept myself, even though I have anxiety" or "I accept myself with these anxiety sensations: [*specify sensations*]." Or perhaps "Even though I have anxiety, I choose to feel calm and secure." Although this serves to treat psychological reversal, remember that in EFT it's called the setup statement. (Note: Throughout this chapter, the reversal and setup statements are varied to illustrate other choices that may be considered, depending on your inclination.)

3. Tap the following EFT points while observing the anxiety sensations and using a reminder phrase at each point:

   • Eyebrow (EB)

   • Side of eye (SE)

   • Under eye (UE)

   • Under nose (UN)

   • Under bottom lip (UL)

   • Under collarbone (UCB)

   • Under arm (UA)

   • Inside wrist (IW)

   • Top of head (TOH)

4. The reminder phrases should target the specific issue at hand, whether it's fear of having a heart attack, worry about family, stress at work, and so forth. For example, if the anxiety is about performance at work, the setup statement might be "Even though I have worry and anxiety about my performance at work, I accept myself," and the reminder phrase would be "worry and anxiety about my performance at work."

Consider doing 4-8 breathing after completing the sequence. (Note: 4-8 breathing is optional, since it is not used in standard EFT.)

5. Rate your anxiety again. If it has not decreased by at least two points, go back to step 2 and repeat the sequence. Persistence generally pays off. If there is no decrease after three attempts, see chapter 5 for troubleshooting options. Once your anxiety has decreased by two or more points, continue to the next step.

6. At this time, you might do the 9G treatments by tapping repeatedly at the back of the hand (BH) while doing the following: close your eyes, open your eyes, look down and to the left, look down and to the right, rotate your eyes clockwise, rotate your eyes counterclockwise, hum a tune, count to five, and then hum again. (Note: The 9G is optional, since it is not used in standard EFT.)

7. Rate your anxiety level again. Although there is often a decrease, proceed even if there is no decrease.

8. Repeat each EFT tapping point with the accompanying reminder phrase, and consider 4-8 breathing.

9. Again, rate your anxiety level. As long as there is a decrease in the SUD level, continue with this protocol until the anxiety is within the 0–2 range. If the treatment stalls at any point, this may indicate a mini reversal. Treat this by tapping the little-finger side of the hand (SH) while saying three times, "I deeply accept myself, even though I still have some of this anxiety" or "Even though I still have some anxiety, I choose to feel better." This treatment may need to be repeated several times before there is complete or near-complete relief.

10. When the anxiety level is 0 to 2, do the floor-to-ceiling eye roll (ER) to lower the anxiety further or to complete the treatment effects. To do this, tap on the back of the hand (BH), hold your head straight, and using only your eyes, look at the floor and then slowly and steadily raise your eyes up toward the ceiling. Check your SUD rating again, and repeat ER as needed. Optionally, consider elaborated eye roll (EER). (Note: The ER and EER are optional, since they are not standard in EFT.)

11. Challenge the results by trying to get the anxiety back. If it isn't possible, great! If anxiety returns, repeat the treatment with the understanding that practice makes perfect.

12. Consider applying the outcome projection procedure (OPP) by tapping on the back of the hand (BH) while installing the conviction that you will continue to feel well. Check your level of conviction (with 10 being the strongest) periodically while you tap. (Note: OPP is optional, since it is not used in standard EFT.)

13. If the feelings of anxiety should return at a later time, repeat these treatments. In time, recurrence of anxiety symptoms will become less frequent.

14. Debriefing: If you are working with a client, show them how to use the protocol between sessions.

Phobias

Specific Phobia

While there are many different phobias, the most basic type is a specific phobia, which involves an intense and irrational fear about a particular object or situation. You might have a specific phobia of dogs (cynophobia), mice (musophobia), dirt (mysophobia), birds (ornithophobia), insects (entomophobia), water (hydrophobia), blood (hematophobia), or clowns (coulrophobia), to name a few. Some phobias are more complex than others. For example, fear of flying (aerophobia) can involve multiple elements, such as fear of being in an enclosed space (claustrophobia), fear of crashing (dystychiphobia), fear of dying (thanatophobia), fear of heights (acrophobia), and fear of crowds (agoraphobia).

In contrast to most other anxiety disorders, specific phobias involve a fear reaction that is practically immediate and not necessarily preceded by a conscious thought. It's basically a stimulus-response (S-R) reaction. You see a spider, and you immediately react by running away or freezing. Or you see a needle, and you become lightheaded and pass out. This type of response might be useful if you were facing a real and imminent threat, but in the case of a phobia, the reaction is disproportionate to any likely danger.

One of the earliest studies on the effectiveness of tapping for specific phobias involved EFT, and it focused on specific phobias of small animals. Compared to patients who were treated with diaphragmatic breathing, those who were treated with EFT showed greater improvement for EFT that was maintained, and possibly enhanced, up to nine months after treatment (Wells et al., 2003). Additional studies have since supported the efficiency of tapping to treat specific phobias (Baker & Siegel, 2010; Lambrou et al., 2005).

When tapping for a specific phobia, there will be a difference in strategy depending on the complexity of the phobia. However, the tapping routine itself can follow the basic form developed by Callahan, modified as follows.

Protocol: Specific Phobia

1. Bring the phobia to mind—that is, think about the fear of water, dogs, spiders, heights, enclosed spaces, or whatever else the phobia might be—and rate your SUD level from 0 to 10.

2. Tap on the little-finger side of either hand (SH) or rub the sore spot (SS) on the left side of chest while saying three times, "Even though I have this [state the phobia], I accept myself" or "I accept myself with this [state the phobia]."

3. Tap these points several times each:

   • Under eye (UE)

   • Under arm (UA)

   • Under collarbone (UCB)

   • Under arm (UA)

   • Under eye (UE)

   • Under collarbone (UCB)

4. Check the SUD level again. If it has not decreased by at least two points, repeat steps 2 and 3 until it decreases. Persistence usually pays off. If not, consult chapter 5 for troubleshooting tips. Once the SUD level is lower, proceed to the next step.

5. Do the 9G treatments by tapping at the back of the hand (BH) while doing the following: close your eyes, open your eyes, look down and to the left, look down and to the right, rotate your eyes clockwise, rotate your eyes counterclockwise, hum a tune, count to five, and then hum again.

6. Rate your SUD level again. Although there is often a decrease, proceed even if there is no decrease. Go through the tapping sequence again, alternating between the tapping points and the 9G until the SUD level is in the 0–2 range.

7. When the SUD level is 0 to 2, do the floor-to-ceiling-eye roll (ER) to lower the SUD further or to complete the treatment effects. To do this, tap on the back of the hand (BH), hold your head straight, and using only your eyes, look at the floor and then slowly and steadily raise your eyes up toward the ceiling. Check the SUD level again, and repeat the ER as needed.

8. Challenge the results by trying to get the anxiety back. If it isn't possible, great! If anxiety returns, repeat the treatment with the understanding that practice makes perfect.

9. Consider applying the outcome projection procedure (OPP) by tapping on the back of the hand (BH) while installing the conviction that you will continue to feel well. Check your level of conviction (with 10 being the strongest) periodically while you tap. (Note: OPP is optional, since it is not used in standard TFT.)

10. If the phobic reaction should return at a later time, repeat these treatments in vivo (that is, in the actual presence of the feared object or situation, instead of in your imagination). In time, recurrence of phobic symptoms will become less frequent.

Social Phobia

Unlike most specific phobias, social phobia (or social anxiety disorder) is a more complex phobia that entails many elements or aspects. Individuals with social phobia experience intense anxiety about being in social situations, such as meeting strangers, being observed eating or drinking, or performing in front of others. This anxiety stems from the person's concern that they will be negatively judged by others, rejected, embarrassed, humiliated, or shamed—or possibly that they will offend others.

The tapping routine I just covered for specific phobias can be applied, while focusing on the various elements of social phobia. Otherwise, the MLT, EFT, or TFT routines are also effective. Here are some reversal statements and associated reminder phrases (in italics) to consider:

- "Even though I have *social anxiety*, I accept myself."

- "Even though I have these *anxiety sensations*, I accept myself."

- "Even though I'm afraid of *being judged*, I accept myself."

- "Even though I'm afraid I'll *be rejected*, I accept myself."

- "Even though I'm afraid I'll *be embarrassed*, I accept myself."

- "Even though I'm afraid I'll *be humiliated*, I accept myself."

- "Even though I'm afraid I'll *be shamed*, I accept myself."

- "Even though I'm afraid I'll *offend others*, I accept myself."

Other psychological reversal corrections may be needed as well, such as "Even if I *always* have social phobia [*or specify symptoms*], I accept myself" or "Even if I *deserve* to have social phobia [*or specify symptoms*], I accept myself." It may also be necessary to tap on specific memories of social anxiety, as the individual may have experienced a traumatic or stressful social situation in the past, and the person lives in fear that a similar episode will occur in the future. In this case, treating the traumatic incident is usually essential in order to target the ongoing social anxiety.

Agoraphobia

One of the most debilitating phobias is agoraphobia, which involves fear about being in situations where escape might be difficult, such as using public transportation, being in open or enclosed spaces, standing in line, being in crowds, or leaving the house alone. Because individuals with agoraphobia fear that they will feel panicked, helpless, or embarrassed in these situations, they may become increasingly isolative and begin to avoid doing everyday tasks that require leaving the home.

The tapping routine I covered earlier on specific phobias can be applied, while focusing on the various elements of agoraphobia. Alternatively, the EFT, MLT, or TFT routines are also effective. Here are some reversal statements and associated reminder phrases (in italics) to consider:

- "Even though I have *agoraphobia*, I accept myself, and I choose to feel secure."

- "Even though I have these *anxiety sensations*, I accept myself, and I choose to feel secure."

- "Even though I'm afraid of *using public transportation*, I accept myself, and I can feel secure while using public transportation."

- "Even though I'm afraid of *standing in line*, I accept myself…"

- "Even though I'm afraid of *being in crowds*, I accept myself…"

- "Even though I'm afraid of *being a distance from home*, I accept myself…"

Other psychological reversal corrections may be needed as well, such as "Even if I *always* have agoraphobia [*or specify symptoms*], I accept myself" or "Even if I *deserve* to have agoraphobia [*or specify symptoms*], I accept myself." In addition, if the agoraphobic episodes began in relation to some traumatic event, it is usually necessary to tap on the specific memories of that event in order for treatment to be successful.

Separation Anxiety Disorder

While not specifically considered a phobia, separation anxiety disorder has similarities to agoraphobia in that individuals with this disorder also fear leaving the home. However, with separation anxiety, individuals don't fear that they will become trapped or helpless in panic-inducing situations. Rather, they experience extreme distress when they are separated from their attachment figures—typically the parents or guardians—or when they anticipate being separated from these attachment figures. This anxiety stems from the fear that they will lose their attachment figure, which causes them to worry about events that could lead to separation, have fears being alone, have nightmares about separation, and experience frequent somatic symptoms when separated from the attachment figure.

The tapping routine I covered earlier on specific phobias, MLT, EFT, or TFT can be applied to the treatment of separation anxiety disorder, while using the following reversal statements and associated reminder phrases (in italics):

- "Even though I have *separation anxiety*, I accept myself, and I can feel safe and secure."

- "Even though I have these *anxiety sensations*, I accept myself, and I'm safe and secure."

- "Even though I'm afraid of *being away from home*, I accept myself, and I'm safe and secure."

- "Even though I'm afraid of *being alone*, I accept myself, and I can be safe and secure being alone."

- "Even though I'm afraid of *losing* [*state the safe person*], I accept myself, and I can be safe and secure."

- "Even though I have *nightmares about being separated from* [*state the safe person*], I accept myself, and I can let go of these nightmares."

Other psychological reversal corrections may be needed as well, such as "Even if I *always* have separation anxiety [*or specify symptoms*], I accept myself, and I'm safe and secure" or "Even if I *deserve* to have separation anxiety [*or specify symptoms*], I accept myself, and I'm safe and secure."

Panic Disorder

Panic disorder is a condition in which individuals experience intense surges of anxiety—even terror—that cause a variety of physical symptoms, such as racing heart, sweating, trembling, shortness of breath, tingling, and feelings of derealization or depersonalization. In the throes of a panic attack, the individual may feel that they are having a heart attack or stroke, that they are going to die or go crazy, or that they are going to do something tremendously embarrassing. There may be a subliminal internal or environmental stimulus or cue that triggers the attack, though they can occur out of the blue as well. When there is an identifiable trigger involved, the person will tend to avoid these situations, such as refraining from driving a car if they previously experienced panic attacks while driving.

The tapping routine I covered earlier on specific phobias, MLT, EFT, or TFT can be applied to the treatment of panic disorder, while using the following reversal statements and associated reminder phrases (in italics):

- "Even though I have *panic attacks*, I accept myself."
- "I accept myself with having *panic attacks*."
- "Even though I have *panic attacks*, I'll be okay."
- "Even though I have this *derealization* experience, I accept myself."
- "Even though I have this *depersonalization* experience, I accept myself."
- "Even though I have these *panic sensations*, I accept myself."
- "Even though I'm afraid I'm *going to die*, I accept myself."
- "Even though I'm afraid I'll *go crazy*, I accept myself."
- "Even if the panic *won't stop*, I accept myself."

Other psychological reversal corrections may be needed as well, such as "Even if I *always* have panic attacks [*or specify symptoms*], I accept myself" or "Even if I *deserve* to have panic attacks [*or specify symptoms*], I accept myself." In addition to tapping, it is also helpful to apply mindfulness techniques during panic episodes. This involves practicing acceptance and nonjudgment, observing the ebb and flow of the panic sensations, and maintaining awareness that the episode will eventually pass. Here are the steps to follow.

Protocol: Panic Disorder

1. Treat for psychological reversal by tapping the little-finger side of the hand or rubbing the sore spot (SS) while saying, "I accept myself with these panic sensations, and I can do this." Then tap on the MLT or EFT points throughout the experience.

2. Know that you had a thought, either consciously or as a result of unconscious neuroception, and that your body is now reacting to that thought with a sense of danger that is not valid. You are not going crazy, you are not going to die, and you are not going to fall apart.

3. Focus on accepting and observing the emotional and physical sensations of the panic, including its location, shape, and intensity (0 to 10). Call out the changes as they occur. For example: "Now it's a 7 and in my stomach… now a 5 and in my neck… now an 8 and in my stomach and chest… now a 2…" The intensity will ebb and flow, as will the images of the sensations.

4. Remind yourself that the panic will eventually subside; it will not go on forever. Panic always passes.

Other Treatment Considerations

Once you've worked on tapping to reduce anxiety, you can also use certain cognitive treatments to further solidify the treatment effects. However, it is important to use these interventions only after engaging in tapping. That's because tapping serves to the reduce the energetic disruptions caused by anxiety, leaving you with more energy for the more evolved areas of the brain involved in higher thinking, specifically the frontal lobes. This makes it easier for people to understand and appreciate these commonsense principles.

One cognitive intervention involves helping clients understand that although anxiety symptoms are unsettling and uncomfortable, they are not hazardous or dangerous. It's also helpful to understand that anxiety is a stress response that occurs a result of scary thoughts or worry. I like to point out that the vagus nerve and the more primitive areas of the brain cannot tell the difference between a real danger and an imagined one, so when we worry, the body reacts as if there is real danger. This accounts for the unsettling anxiety symptoms, which will pass as you drop the thoughts and use the tapping and breathing exercises.

Most people can also appreciate the fact that the vast majority of things they worry about never occur. I might even recommend jotting down a list of worries and checking them off whenever a worry comes true. Usually, people discover a clean slate with no check marks (or very few).

I also like to explain that while higher-order thought makes it possible for us to achieve and create things, it is a double-edged sword. Thoughts can help or hurt us, depending on our level of understanding of thought. It's useful to understand that thoughts are not real in a concrete sense. They are essentially illusions or mirages. And they have no power over us unless we give our power over to them. Of course, this realization also occurs in thought form, so here we're essentially fighting fire with fire.

There are an infinite number of realizations that can seal in your level of understanding and promote more security. As anxiety passes, common sense and wisdom become readily available. Tap into and realize your personal power.

Chapter 10

The Future of Tapping

The glory of giving blessings to others is that the blessings don't go just to one person. They spread like sparks of fire. They touch other beings and other parts of the earth, also.

—Gurumayi Chidvilasananda

When I published the first edition of *Energy Psychology* in 1998, I made a number of predictions regarding the future of tapping that have already come to fruition. At the time, there was already some research into this methodology, but it wasn't difficult to predict that more research would occur. As of 2021, over 245 review articles, research studies, and meta-analyses have been published in refereed journals comparing the effectiveness of EP with other therapies. While those of us in the field knew that tapping was highly effective long before solid research was available, it is gratifying to see the evidence now mounting and confirming what we have personally experienced. I also predicted that tapping would soon be used for the treatment of addiction, depression, dissociative identity disorder, GAD, OCD, panic, phobias, allergies, substance sensitivities, physical pain, and various medical conditions—and this has occurred.

In my view, EP, tapping, and interrelated techniques will become increasingly mainstream, not only in the fields of therapy and coaching, but also in schools, hospitals, sports programs, and more. These techniques are bound to enter the mainstream because of their efficiency and also because there is a great need that exists throughout the world. Many existing therapies do not get results quickly, and some are not suited to treating particular problems. Certain therapies can even result in re-traumatization and make the condition worse, which is very unlikely to occur with competent use of EP and tapping techniques like TFT, EFT, and MLT. And while some problems inevitably take more time to treat, there are many conditions that should and can be resolved fairly quickly with

EP and tapping. As more people come to this realization, I believe they will be inclined to pursue these brief, highly effective therapies.

I also believe that tapping will become applicable in many medical areas as a way of promoting healing and preventing health problems. I have found this to be true in my own experience, after being diagnosed with "terminal" mantle cell lymphoma (MCL) in December 2005 after a tumor was removed from my neck. Before seeing an oncologist, I regularly treated myself holistically with EP tapping, reversal corrections, switching corrections like the hookup, dietary changes, and baths to reduce acidity and inflammation. After 24 months, the blood tests, physical exams, PET scans, and bone marrow biopsy revealed no cancer. I continued to be monitored for eight years, during which no cancer was detected. Fifteen years later, I developed another neck tumor that was considered to be so indolent that the oncologist concluded that we could either simply keep a watchful eye on it or perhaps do some low-level radiation to prevent other tumors from developing. I opted for the radiation and continued to do self-treatment with EP. A year later, a PET scan revealed no cancer activity.

I realize that I am a single case, but perhaps this points the way to the application of EP and tapping, combined with traditional and alternative approaches, in the treatment of some cancers and other terminal diseases. Possibly, people who survive terminal diseases have certain characteristics—such as the conviction that their disease will not be their demise—are surrounded by friends and family who believe the same, follow their doctor's advice, and go above and beyond with EP and other complementary approaches. Although we don't have any randomized controlled trials on this possibility, it makes intimate sense to me, and I predict that this will be researched and found to be beneficial.

Ultimately, though, the future of EP and tapping is up to us. As a first step, you can apply these concepts and techniques to elevate your health and well-being—and, in turn, your state will resonate with and touch the lives of others. Be a source of inspiration. Spread goodwill and good health. Together we can make this happen.

Appendix

Recommended Readings and Resources

Books

Banks, S. (1998). *The missing link: Reflections on philosophy and spirit.* Lone Pine.

Banks, S. (2001). *The enlightened gardener.* Lone Pine.

Becker, R. O., & Selden, G. (1985). *The body electric: Electromagnetism and the foundation of life.* Quill.

Bilazarian, R. W. (2018). *Tapping the mighty mind: Simple solutions for stress, conflict, and pain.* CreateSpace.

Burr, H. S. (1972). *Blueprint for immortality: The electric patterns of life.* Saffron Walden.

Callahan, R. J. (with Trubo, R.). (2001). *Tapping the healer within: Using thought field therapy to instantly conquer your fears, anxieties, and emotional distress.* Contemporary Books.

Church, D. (2013). *The EFT manual* (3rd ed.). Energy Psychology Press.

Diepold, J. H., Jr. (2018). *Heart assisted therapy: Integrating heart energy to facilitate emotional health, healing, and performance enhancement.* Outskirts Press.

Feinstein, D. (2004). *Energy psychology interactive: Rapid interventions for lasting change.* Innersource.

Feinstein, D., Eden, D., & Craig, G. (2005). *The promise of energy psychology: Revolutionary tools for dramatic personal change.* Penguin.

Furman, M., & Gallo, F. (2000). *The neurophysics of human behavior: Explorations at the interface of brain, mind, behavior, and information.* CRC Press.

Gallo, F. P. (2000). *Energy diagnostic and treatment methods.* W. W. Norton.

Gallo, F. P. (Ed.). (2002). *Energy psychology in psychotherapy: A comprehensive sourcebook*. W. W. Norton.

Gallo, F. P. (2005). *Energy psychology: Explorations at the interface of energy, cognition, behavior, and health* (2nd ed.). CRC Press.

Gallo, F. P. (2007). *Energy tapping for trauma: Rapid relief from post-traumatic stress using energy psychology*. New Harbinger.

Gallo, F. P., & Vincenzi, H. (2008). *Energy tapping: How to rapidly eliminate anxiety, depression, cravings, and more using energy psychology* (2nd ed.). New Harbinger.

Hartung, J. G., & Galvin, M. D. (2003). *Energy psychology and EMDR: Combining forces to optimize treatment*. W. W. Norton.

Hover-Kramer, D. (2002). *Creative energies: Integrative energy psychotherapy for self-expression and healing*. W. W. Norton.

Porges, S. W. (2011). *The polyvagal theory: Neurobiological foundations of emotions, attachment, communication, and self-regulation*. W. W. Norton.

Pransky, G. S. (1992). *Divorce is not the answer: A change of heart will save your marriage*. HIS and TAB Books.

Rogers, C. R. (1961). *On becoming a person: A therapist's view of psychotherapy*. Houghton Mifflin.

Wells, S., & Lake, D. (2010). *Enjoy emotional freedom: Simple techniques for living life to the full*. Exisle Publishing.

Articles

Feinstein, D. (2019). Energy psychology: Efficacy, speed, mechanisms. *Explore*, *15*(5), 340–351. https://doi.org/10.1016/j.explore.2018.11.003

Feinstein, D. (2021). Six empirically-supported premises about energy psychology: Mounting evidence for a controversial therapy. *Advances in Mind-Body Medicine*, *35*(2), 17–32. https://advances-journal.com/wp-content/uploads/2021/05/Feinstein.pdf

Websites

Association for Comprehensive Energy Psychology (ACEP): energypsych.org

Canadian Association for Integrative and Energy Therapies (CAIET): caiet.org

Eden Energy Medicine: innersource.net

EFT International (EFTI; formerly AAMET): eftinternational.org

EFT Universe: eftuniverse.com

Fred P. Gallo's Energy Psychology site: energypsych.com

Gary Craig's EFT Training Centers: emofree.com

Institute of Noetic Sciences (IONS): noetic.org

TFT Foundation: tftfoundation.org

PESI and PESI Publishing: pesi.com

References

Andrade, J., & Feinstein, D. (2004). Energy psychology: Theory, indications, and evidence. In D. Feinstein (Ed.), *Energy psychology interactive* [CD]. Innersource.

Baker, A. H., & Siegel, L. S. (2010). Emotional freedom techniques (EFT) reduces intense fears: A partial replication and extension of Wells, Polglase, Andrews, Carrington, & Baker (2003). *Energy Psychology: Theory, Research & Treatment, 2*(2), 13–30.

Banks, S. (1998). *The missing link: Reflections on philosophy and spirit.* Lone Pine.

Banks, S. (2001). *The enlightened gardener.* Lone Pine.

Becker, R. O. (1990). *Cross currents: The perils of electropollution, the promise of electromedicine.* Jeremy P. Tarcher.

Becker, R. O., & Selden, G. (1985). *The body electric: Electromagnetism and the foundation of life.* Quill.

Bilazarian, R. W. (2018). *Tapping the mighty mind: Simple solutions for stress, conflict, and pain.* CreateSpace.

Bohm, D. (1980). *Wholeness and the implicate order.* Routledge & Kegan Paul.

Bohm, D., & Hiley, B. J. (1993). *The undivided universe: An ontological interpretation of quantum theory.* Routledge & Kegan Paul.

Callahan, R. J. (1985). *Five minute phobia cure: Dr. Callahan's treatment for fears, phobias and self-sabotage.* Enterprise.

Callahan, R. J. (1987, Winter). Successful psychotherapy by radio and telephone. *International College of Applied Kinesiology.*

Callahan, R. J. (1990). *The rapid treatment of panic, agoraphobia, and anxiety.* Author.

Callahan, R. J. (with Trubo, R.). (2001). *Tapping the healer within: Using thought field therapy to instantly conquer your fears, anxieties, and emotional distress.* Contemporary Books.

Chang, S. T. (1976). *The complete book of acupuncture.* Celestial Arts.

Church, D., Stapleton, P., Kip, K., & Gallo, F. P. (2020). Corrigendum to: Is tapping on acupuncture points an active ingredient in emotional freedom techniques? A systematic review and meta-analysis of comparative studies. *Journal of Nervous and Mental Disease, 208*(8), 632–635. https://doi.org/10.1097/nmd.0000000000001222

Clond, M. (2016). Emotional freedom techniques for anxiety: A systematic review with meta-analysis. *Journal of Nervous and Mental Disease, 204*(5), 388–395. https://doi.org/10.1097/nmd.0000000000000483

Dana, D. (2018). *The polyvagal theory in therapy: Engaging the rhythm of regulation*. W. W. Norton.

de Vernejoul, P., Albarède, P., & Darras, J. C. (1985). Study of the acupuncture meridians with radioactive tracers. *Bulletin of the Academy of National Medicine, 169*, 1071–1075.

de Vernejoul, P., Darras, J. C., Beguin, C., Cazalaa, J. B., Daury, G., & de Vernejoul, J. (1984). Approche isotopique de la visualisation des méridiens d'acupuncture [Isotopic approach to the visualization of acupuncture meridians]. *Agressologic, 25*(10), 1107–1111.

Ecker, B. (2015). Memory reconsolidation understood and misunderstood. *International Journal of Neuropsychotherapy, 3*(1), 2–46. http://dx.doi.org/10.12744/ijnpt.2015.0002-0046

Feinstein, D. (2021). Six empirically-supported premises about energy psychology: Mounting evidence for a controversial therapy. *Advances in Mind-Body Medicine, 35*(2), 17–32. https://advances-journal.com/wp-content/uploads/2021/05/Feinstein.pdf

Frankl, V. E. (1946). *Man's search for meaning: An introduction to logotherapy*. Beacon Press.

Fuller, R. B. (1961). Tensegrity. *Portfolio and Art News Annual, (4)*, 112–127, 144, 148.

Gallo, F. P. (1998). *Energy psychology: Explorations at the interface of energy, cognition, behavior, and health*. CRC Press.

Gallo, F. P. (2000). *Energy diagnostic and treatment methods*. W. W. Norton.

Gallo, F. P. (2005). *Energy psychology: Explorations at the interface of energy, cognition, behavior, and health* (2nd ed.). CRC Press.

Gazzaniga, M. S., & LeDoux, J. E. (1978). *The integrated mind*. Plenum Press.

Gilomen, S. A., & Lee, C. W. (2015). The efficacy of acupoint stimulation in the treatment of psychological distress: A meta-analysis. *Journal of Behavior Therapy and Experimental Psychiatry, 48*, 140–148. https://doi.org/10.1016/j.jbtep.2015.03.012

Lambrou, P., Pratt, G., & Chevalier, G. (2005). Physiological and psychological effects of a mind/body therapy on claustrophobia. *Subtle Energies & Energy Medicine, 14*(3), 239–251. https://journals.sfu.ca/seemj/index.php/seemj/article/view/367/329

Langman, L. (1972). The implications of the electro-metric test in cancer of the female genital tract. In H. S. Burr (Ed.), *Blueprint for immortality: The electric patterns of life* (pp. 137–154). Saffron Walden.

Leonoff, G. (1995). The successful treatment of phobias and anxiety by telephone and radio: A replication of Callahan's 1987 study. *TFT Newsletter, 1*(2), 1, 6.

Melzack, R., & Wall, P. D. (1965). Pain mechanisms: A new theory. *Science, 150*(3699), 971–979. https://doi.org/10.1126/science.150.3699.971

Melzack, R., & Wall, P. D. (1982). *The challenge of pain.* Basic Books.

Nelms, J., & Castel, L. (2016). A systematic review and meta-analysis of randomized and nonrandomized trials of emotional freedom techniques (EFT) for the treatment of depression. *Explore, 12*(6), 416–426. https://doi.org/10.1016/j.explore.2016.08.001

Porges, S. W. (2011). *The polyvagal theory: Neurobiological foundation of emotions, attachment, communication, and self-regulation.* W. W. Norton.

Pransky, G. S. (1992). *Divorce is not the answer: A change of heart will save your marriage.* HIS and TAB Books.

Reichmanis, M., Marino, A. A., & Becker, R. O. (1975). Electrical correlates of acupuncture points. *IEEE Transactions on Biomedical Engineering, 22*(6), 533–535. https://doi.org/10.1109/TBME.1975.324477

Rogers, C. R. (1951). *Client-centered therapy: its current practice, implications, and theory.* Houghton Mifflin.

Schore, A. N. (1994). *Affect regulation and the origin of the self: The neurobiology of emotional development.* Lawrence Erlbaum.

Sebastian, B., & Nelms, J. (2017). The effectiveness of emotional freedom techniques in the treatment of posttraumatic stress disorder: A meta-analysis. *Explore, 13*(1), 16–25. https://doi.org/10.1016/j.explore.2016.10.001

Song, H.-S., & Lehrer, P. M. (2003). The effects of specific respiratory rates on heart rate and heart rate variability. *Applied Psychophysiology and Biofeedback, 28*(1), 13–23. https://doi.org/10.1023/a:1022312815649

Terr, L. (1994). *Unchained memories: True stories of traumatic memories, lost and found.* Basic Books.

Walther, D. S. (1988). *Applied kinesiology: Synopsis.* Systems DC.

Warren, S. (2019). *The pain relief secret: How to retrain your nervous system, heal your body, and overcome chronic pain.* TCK Publishing.

Wells, S., Polglase, K., Andrews, H. B., Carrington, P., & Baker, A. H. (2003). Evaluation of a meridian-based intervention, emotional freedom techniques (EFT), for reducing specific phobias of small animals. *Journal of Clinical Psychology, 59*(9), 943–966. https://doi.org/10.1002/jclp.10189

Made in United States
Orlando, FL
19 October 2023